mental health services

Royal College of
Occupational
Therapists

WITHDRAWN

heading for better care

**COMMISSIONING AND PROVIDING MENTAL HEALTH SERVICES FOR
PEOPLE WITH HUNTINGTON'S DISEASE, ACQUIRED BRAIN INJURY
AND EARLY ONSET DEMENTIA**

London HMSO

HEADING FOR BETTER CARE

EDITORS

Dr Richard Williams

Dr Ken Barrett

Mrs Zena Muth

AUTHORS

Dr Willy Barker

Dr Ken Barrett

Mr William Bingley

Dr Neil Brooks

Ms Jill Cox

Dr Stuart Cumella

Mr Giles Emerson

Mr Clive Evers

Mr Mike Gardiner

Dr Richard Williams

CHAPTER I

The Director's
Introduction

THE BENEFIT OF A FOCUSED APPROACH

I   In recent years, the NHS Health Advisory Service (HAS) has embarked on a number of projects that have covered large sectors of the population and a very diverse range of services. Its report, *Together We Stand*, for example, covered mental health services for children and adolescents from birth to young adulthood. Inevitably, such a project demanded considerable shaping and co-ordination in order to make sense of the vast amount of information derived from the analysis of contemporary research and numerous service visits. With this report, we are more fortunate, for two reasons.

2   First, the HAS is dealing here with patients in just three groups or patterns of disease or brain injury: Huntington's Disease; acquired brain injury; and early onset dementia. Each of these groups is well represented by a leading voluntary charitable organisation, which has been a valuable source of information and advice; and the number of patients affected across all three groups across the country is relatively low as a proportion of the whole population. This has allowed the HAS to be highly focused in the information-gathering process during the review, and equally focused in our recommendations for service improvements.

3   Second, this review benefits to a considerable extent from the wealth of material previously gathered in other recent thematic reviews, particularly concerning the development of commissioning strategies and purchasing techniques. Consequently, we have been able to incorporate a certain amount of background material, learned from other reviews and already to some extent tried and tested by commissioners and providers in other fields. For example, we provide advice on legal issues affecting the design and delivery of services, and advice about workable strategies that concern training and staffing issues.

4   Across all the thematic reviews, a number of common themes have arisen and, with the benefit of experience, we have been able to give appropriate weight to each of these themes in this report. The main themes include:

- the importance of taking user and carer views into account in the planning and delivery of services;

- the importance of developing a sound knowledge-base upon which to develop strategy and service delivery;

- the importance of developing fruitful partnerships with other statutory and non-statutory agencies, including social services, voluntary organisations and private sector care agencies;

- the importance of inter-agency, inter-disciplinary and multi-disciplinary working, and the establishment – at both commissioning and providing levels – of the means to ensure there is good inter-disciplinary communication;

- the importance of joint commissioning, between health and local authorities, as well as between different health authorities, particularly where highly specialised, supra-district services are involved;

- the importance of establishing appropriate care pathways and referral systems for individual patients so that care may be provided seamlessly by the diversity of agencies involved - from acute medical and mental health services to subsequent rehabilitation, therapy and domiciliary support; and

- the importance of setting goals and measuring outcomes to keep track of progress and to enable the refinement of strategy and, thereby, further improvements in the services that are provided.

5   All these factors are covered in this report, among many others that relate specifically to the three client groups. Of all of these common factors, the first listed above is critically important to these client groups. Although there are relatively few people in the country who have Huntington's Disease, acquired brain injury and early onset dementia, those people with these disorders make demands on health authorities and social services departments that are disproportionate to their numbers. Not only this, but a service that is not provided early on can be a hidden source of additional expenditure later. But most of all, people with these conditions require the devoted attention of carers, who are usually women and close family relatives. For example, most acquired brain injuries happen to males aged 15 to 30, and, while they may be severely disabled by the injury, their longevity is seldom affected once past the immediate crisis. Therefore, they require close care and support for a great many years. Equally, early onset dementia and Huntington's Disease can affect people from their fourth decade onwards and carers may be in harness for two decades or more looking after them. Not surprisingly, the effect on family carers can be extreme, with clinical depression and other conditions resulting from stress, anxiety, uncertainty and change in the feelings and behaviour of close relatives. In the planning and restructuring of services proposed in this report, the needs of carers cannot be stressed enough.

6   In tandem with this, it becomes highly important for health authorities to ensure that there are clear links and referral processes between GPs, neurologists, psychiatrists and the community mental health services that deal with patients in these groups. When the process breaks down, as has happened too often, cumulative delays occur denying patients access to treatment and putting unnecessary stress on carers.

A QUESTION OF REDIRECTING RESOURCES

7   The HAS review teams visited six different districts and interviewed, among many others, users, carers, clinicians, commissioning managers, social workers, officials from local branches of major voluntary organisations, GPs, practice and community psychiatric nurses, and professionals allied to medicine. While the reviewers considered that none of the districts had comprehensive services for all three client groups, they found good examples of services for one or more of these groups in most of the districts that were visited. They also found examples of particularly good practice and have used these as a basis for developing the service models that are described in this report.

8   The experiences of the reviewers in conducting these visits have confirmed to the HAS the importance of effective services for people in each of these client groups. In each, patients may experience significant problems of co-morbidity of psychiatric disorders with the index disease or injury. Awareness of these and the long-term nature of

each patient's requirement for services, has implications for planning priorities.

9   In the review teams' analysis of the services being provided, a common, and certainly hopeful, finding was that improvements could be made by adjusting or aligning service structures, sometimes involving the redirection of resources, rather than necessarily calling for additional funds. Inevitably, additional funds could be used to make even greater improvements, but the principle here is that it is effective service organisation not money that is needed as a priority.

A TOOL FOR OTHER DEVELOPMENTS

10   This report focuses on relatively small groups of patients who have particular needs, but these groups were chosen for two main reasons. First, their needs have been neglected in healthcare planning for too long and, second, these client groups serve as templates for approaching the development of services for other definable groups of patients, particularly those in which patients have other brain diseases and other neuropsychiatric disorders. Certain elements of service development for particular groups of patients will inevitably be similar to those advocated here. For example, commissioners of any such services should plan their strategies on the basis of accurate locally-derived knowledge of prevalence, and providers should tailor programmes of care according to the clinically understood patterns of patient needs. Not only this, but the challenges facing providers of health and social care are similar to those presented by a range of other conditions that have long-term psycho-social impacts.

ACKNOWLEDGEMENTS

11   I would like to thank the members of the expert advisory group, the editors, authors of this report and the service visitors who have put enormous time and effort into carrying out the review and preparing this report. They have brought remarkable expertise to bear, conducted the tasks set by the review quickly and worked together creatively to produce practical solutions to challenging problems. Throughout, they have sought to find durable answers to complex matters. The HAS owes much to each of them. They are listed in Annex E at the back of this publication.

12   I would particularly like to single out Dr Ken Barrett who agreed to act as my leading adviser and author. He has supported me, the staff of the HAS and our secondees with tireless humour throughout, though I have tested his good nature with short deadlines and naive questions. Additionally, his calm approach has been an enormous asset in gaining the co-operation of so many other people. His expertise and the standing and respect in which he is held by fellow professionals in the field of neuropsychiatry has proved invaluable. Ken has shown his mettle in the task of writing this report. He has been willing to put countless hours into writing and re-writing certain chapters, and into checking the accuracy of the whole text. I am very grateful to him.

13   All the members of my expert advisory group have worked together in a way that models well the true spirit of multi-disciplinary co-operation and team work.

14   Also, I acknowledge the expert advice of Professor Wilson, of the University of Liverpool Medical School and Dr Prasher, a Consultant in Learning Disability in Birmingham.

15   I am also grateful to the professional colleagues and the managers of services in which all the individuals who have contributed to this review are usually employed, for their forbearance in allowing them leave of absence to carry out the review.

16   Not least, I am grateful to all the managers, clinicians and other workers in the six districts visited, for giving substantial time to the review teams during the field visits.

17   The voluntary organisations, in particular the Alzheimer's Disease Society, the Huntington's Disease Association and Headway, play a strong part in the provision of mental health services for this group of patients. In many parts of the country, they are the main providers of specialist daycare facilities, usually on a contractual basis with health and local authorities, and will remain important in the equation of overall provision in the future. I would particularly like to thank representatives of these organisations for their invaluable assistance in the preparation of this report.

Richard Williams

Director

NHS Health Advisory Service

August 1996

18 This report discloses the findings and recommendations of the HAS review which sets out to evaluate the prevailing state of mental health services for people with three particular disorders: acquired brain injury (ABI); early onset dementia; and Huntington's Disease (HD).

19 Although there are relatively low numbers of people suffering from these disorders in a given population, they have a major impact on health and social services, voluntary organisations and carers within families. While each of these disorders has different symptoms and consequences, all three have certain features in common:

- they are characterised by severe, and often progressive, physical, psychological and behavioural impairments;

- they have a profound impact on the lives and capabilities of those who develop these disorders and their carers; and

- they require major long-term commitments from both health and social care services.

20 At primary healthcare level, GPs, practice nurses, social workers and other professionals may not have any experience of treating individuals with one or more of these particular disorders. Because of the relatively low incidence of people with these disorders at local level, together with the lack of specialised hospital, residential or nursing home facilities for these groups, many people with ABI, early onset dementia and HD receive inappropriate care. They are, for example, sometimes inappropriately placed in acute hospital wards (both medical and psychiatric), nursing homes for elderly mentally ill people, and private hospitals located far away from their families.

21 Sometimes, patients with ABI and HD are categorised as having predominantly physical disorders and this can result in insufficient care for psychiatric, behavioural, emotional and cognitive problems that often develop. In fact, people with brain disease and brain damage are at greater risk of mental health problems and disorders than the general population. Their carers are also more liable to depression and other illnesses resulting from the stress of providing care to a close relative or friend whose life and personality has changed.

22 All three disorders are, however, well represented by nationally networked voluntary and charitable organisations, in particular the Huntington's Disease Association (HDA), the Alzheimer's Disease Society (ADS) and Headway. These organisations have played an increasingly important role in supporting sufferers and their carers, and in providing updated information about the disorders to primary healthcare teams. The HAS review teams noted examples of good practice where these voluntary organisations were commissioned by health and social services to supplement providers in the statutory sector.

23 The HAS visited six districts in England and Wales in the process of the review and gleaned information from health authorities, social services departments, voluntary organisations, and users and carers. Thus, it was able to generate a picture of current service shortcomings and strengths which would reasonably represent the picture at national level.

24   Carers of people with ABI, early onset dementia and HD, as well as users of services themselves, indicated the following key problems to the HAS.

- Lack of expert assessment and inaccurate diagnosis of behaviour problems, often resulting from the paucity of specialist expertise. While ABI users and carers acknowledged the attention given to them by health professionals, they felt the condition of ABI was often misunderstood. Carers for people with early onset dementia were particularly concerned that the diagnosis should be made as early as possible. Many felt guilty, with hindsight, about their responses to problems in the undiagnosed individuals.

- After the initial acute treatment phase, there was concern about the lack of facilities for rehabilitation, respite care, and support. Patients were often placed in facilities which did not offer rehabilitation. A lack of residential respite care facilities was commonly mentioned by carers of people with early onset dementia. Often, they reported that the only respite care they had been offered was in a home for elderly people with dementia or in an acute psychiatric unit.

- Difficulty in finding specialist information and advice was also a problem reported to HAS reviewers. A frequent comment was that GPs should be given more information about services in order to pass this on to users and carers.

- HD users and carers persistently reported a lack of sufficient centres of expertise and specialism and, conversely, the excellent value of those that do exist, in assisting HD sufferers and carers. HD carers and their families were also particularly keen to receive information, advice and genetic counselling services, given the high risk of HD sufferers' children inheriting the disease. Genetic counselling is also becoming increasingly important to the families of younger people with Alzheimer's Disease.

- Carers of people with HD and early onset dementia were also keen to see continuity in the care provided. For example, a specialist unit that accepts a patient with HD on a daycare basis, is later well placed to take on the same patient as a residential client, with both patient and staff benefiting from the familiarity.

- Carers indicated that poor service articulation can present major problems for patients and family carers, particularly at times of care transitions when a patient is passed from one service to another. They highlighted the need for properly defined care pathways without which there tended to be problems such as failure to complete comprehensive assessments, delays in referral, and confusion and distress for patients and carers.

25   Carers reported favourably the support provided to them by certain professionals and services. Community mental health service teams were found to be particularly supportive. Regular visits from a community psychiatric nurse helped to provide continuity with the breadth of available health services, as well as opportunities for regular reviews of individual patients.

26   The visiting teams found that none of the six districts visited had a comprehensive range of services for all three of these user groups.

Some had well developed services for one or two groups but no specialist service for the remainder. Equally, reviewers found plenty of examples of good practice throughout the six districts.

27 The visiting teams reported that the most dynamic force for change and improvement was the existence of a clinical team with a special interest in one or more of the client groups. Where this was the case, the services in the district tended to focus their efforts on gathering information about requirements, providing advice and support to family carers and primary healthcare teams, building links with other specialist services (such as neurology, genetics and psychiatry of old age), and developing new services in alliance with charities and the independent sector. Where no specialist teams were apparent, the health and social services often relied on the local branches of the leading charitable organisations (ADS, HDA and Headway).

28 Five of the six districts visited have specialist inpatient units which admit people with ABI, HD and early onset dementia alongside people with a number of other conditions. Indeed, one of the main reasons for choosing these five districts was to visit areas in which there are established centres of specialist expertise in order to find examples of good practice. The sixth district was chosen as a reference site to represent the majority of districts that have no specialised services for any of these three client groups.

29 Nonetheless, the visiting teams found no standard model of patient care and considerable variation in the categories of patients admitted, treatment programmes and criteria for discharge. In the sixth district, these groups of patients were admitted to a range of local facilities, including psychiatric wards and psychogeriatric beds. The professionals in most districts, the members of the HAS review teams, and the HAS itself consider this approach inappropriate.

30 Most specialist psychiatric services for these three client groups have a strong inpatient focus with limited outreach services. As a result, they tend to have limited impact on the populations and services of health districts outside their immediate vicinity.

31 The main providers of specialist daycare for these groups are the principal charities. Usually, this is provided on the basis of contracts with the health and social services.

32 In the main, the HAS teams reported that the development of commissioning strategies for these groups of patients, and particularly the development of joint health and social service commissioning, were in their early stages. The main obstacles to development appeared to be:

- the demand placed on commissioning authorities by other priorities;

- the lack of specialist commissioning and provider skills;

- fragmentation of commissioning; and

- lack of information about numbers and needs.

33 More effective commissioning strategies, based on proper assessments of local needs, could be particularly effective for these groups of disorders because the target population is small and well-defined.

All three sets of disorders are well-defined clinical entities which can usually be diagnosed unequivocally. And, although the exact course of the illness cannot be predicted for each patient, the general pattern of symptoms and needs are similar and familiar within each group, and this makes forward planning easier.

34   In general, effective commissioning requires the re-direction of existing funds, so that these client groups receive appropriate care in appropriate settings, rather than any claim for new money.

35   The HAS notes the effectiveness of the complex care programmes (within the Care Programme Approach) that are being applied to patients with these disorders when they are taken on by mental health services. When well applied, the Care Programme Approach (CPA) can help commissioners and purchasers as well as providers to address the wide range of needs of these patients, and to identify gaps in provision.

36   Of singular importance in the post-diagnosis period is the intervention of care co-ordinators, case managers and link nurses who are able to improve greatly the continuity of care, reduce the stress on carers and lead to the more effective use of health resources (in particular, by preventing crises which result in lengthy hospital admissions). Coupled with these types of intervention, voluntary agencies are already well used to providing daycare support, which is usually less stigmatising than facilities provided in the statutory sector and, therefore, more acceptable to users and carers.

37   The HAS believes that a better developed strategic approach to commissioning and providing services for these groups will lead to a step-change in the quality and appropriateness of services without a proportionate increase in costs. Such an approach should be based on following the natural history of each of the disorders, which shows that the patients' clinical conditions change in relatively predictable ways. This provides a clear basis for service concepts, design, commissioning, purchase and delivery.

38   Some general recommendations concerning the development of an effective commissioning and providing strategy include:

- designating a local leader who has or is willing to acquire some expertise in at least one of these three subjects; also bringing in advice from external experts in these fields;

- basing service strategy and planning on the comprehensive assessment of need (this may be based on national norms, but is more accurate if local information can be obtained);

- consulting service users and carers in order to develop effective provision; they should be seen as pivotal in the development of services;

- recognising that patient and carer needs do not end with the acute stage of diagnosis and management. These patients have long clinical careers and continually demand and/or require health and social services. Continuity of care is essential;

- encouraging and stimulating partnership across statutory and independent sector boundaries, in order to ensure more seamless care for these client groups;

- organising co-ordinated management, through a case management approach whereby each patient is allocated a person who is responsible for the planning and orchestration of care;

- similarly, encouraging the development of appropriate care pathways to improve links between different services and service components; and

- at the strategic level, some consideration should be given to providing suitable training, supervision and support to care staff who work in these complex fields.

39　The HAS also makes a number of recommendations about effective service provision for these client groups.

- In recent years, several specialist neuropsychiatry posts have been established, in which the psychiatrist has specialist neurological as well as behavioural and psychiatric expertise. In districts where these posts exist, services tend to be better orientated to people with brain disease and brain damage, while others with, for example Parkinson's Disease or epilepsy, also receive more appropriate treatment.

- Early referral processes should be encouraged so that patients exhibiting emotional or behaviour problems can be referred to a designated specialist, who is able to carry out a comprehensive assessment of individual need and begin the process of creating a care plan.

- Specialist memory and cognitive dysfunction clinics have developed in the UK as useful referral points for people with early onset dementia. They are run by many different disciplines and offer high quality assessment services. These clinics are particularly useful in identifying the treatable disorders that are present in up to 10% of people with early onset dementia.

- Multi-disciplinary working is also essential in the assessment, care and management of people in these client groups. Alongside medical and nursing staff, important contributions are made by clinical neuropsychologists, occupational therapists, speech and language therapists, physiotherapists, social workers, rehabilitation technicians and others. Skill-sharing and coaching by the professions allied to medicine can extend and improve the durability of therapeutic interventions, making more cost-effective use of relatively scarce therapy resources.

- The integration of specialist social workers into healthcare teams provides individual workers with more specialised knowledge of these conditions and their consequences. It also provides them with knowledge of the most appropriate community-based facilities. The CPA is a very effective mechanism for integrating health and social service aspects of a care package for these patients.

40　Targeting provider managers who are responsible for improved service delivery, this report advocates a number of key principles:

- clinical leadership;

- comprehensive, expert and timely assessment, reassessment and treatment;

- multi-disciplinary working with goal-setting;

- good communication and collaboration between agencies, particularly health, social and education services and the non-statutory sector;

- the application of the Care Programme Approach greatly facilitates achieving the two previous principles;

- a range of care options with procedures for determining responsibility for continuing care;

- support and advocacy for the service user and also, but sometimes separately, for their carers;

- education, support and advice for carers;

- the appointment of care or case managers and co-ordinators (as appropriate).

41   Linking all these factors is the issue of training which is seen as centrally important to the improvement of services for people with brain damage or brain disease. The service visits highlighted the fact that there are centres of great expertise in the management of people who have these conditions, but each has usually developed in isolation, accruing knowledge and experience over several years.

42   The reviewers recommend the development of more informal links between services as a means of disseminating knowledge. They also recommend the development of testable treatment and rehabilitation protocols. While it is not difficult to acquire factual knowledge about these conditions, the sharing of practical skills based on real case examples should be encouraged. A core knowledge of brain function and the consequences of damage should be common to all disciplines; beyond this, supra-district and national training strategies would be useful to determine the relevant training needs for each discipline and how to address them.

43   In brain injury work, there has for some time been a more open and shared approach to training and practice. This reflects the difficulty in singling out particular problems and managing them in isolation. A shared approach is much to be recommended and will help to develop the multi-disciplinary teamwork which is central to caring for these groups of people. The HAS advocates periods of induction training for all new staff in each relevant discipline, combined with the process of learning on the job. Allied to this, formal in-house training should be used to spread information and increase the skill base of team members. All professionals and managers require access to appropriate continuing professional development.

44   There are a number of recognised centres throughout the UK which have developed particular expertise for these client groups. These centres should be approached to train staff when other specialised services are being developed and thereafter.

CHAPTER 3

A Guide to this Report

THE AIMS

45   This report aims to raise awareness about the particular problems faced by people who have acquired brain injury (ABI), early onset dementia and Huntington's Disease (HD). It sets out to provide commissioners and purchasers with sufficient insight into what the HAS perceives to be prevailing challenges to the strategic development of services for people with these conditions. It also sets out a framework for service development. Equally, the report focuses on the challenges facing service providers. Service providers include those in the statutory health and social service sectors, as well as leading voluntary and independent organisations which play such important roles in supporting users and carers with these client groups.

46   A cross-section of clinical disciplines is involved in the treatment, rehabilitation and ongoing support of people with ABI, early onset dementia and HD. These include:

- professionals who provide acute medical and surgical services;

- psychiatrists and neuropsychiatrists;

- psychologists;

- specialists in rehabilitation medicine;

- psychogeriatricians;

- community psychiatric nurses;

- GPs, practice nurses and other primary healthcare workers;

- social workers;

- specialist residential and nursing home workers; and

- a range of the professions allied to medicine, predominately physiotherapists, speech and language therapists, and occupational therapists.

47   The report stresses the importance of the roles of all those involved in the care of these patients and the importance of inter-agency, multi-disciplinary and inter-disciplinary working to achieve the most appropriate services.

48   Not least, the report focuses on the part played by these patients' carers, and their representatives, and how they may be best supported in the vital roles that they perform.

HOW TO USE THIS REPORT

49   The report is intended to provide a combination of reference and factual information about ABI, early onset dementia and HD, as well as suggesting good practice and ideal approaches to commissioning and delivering services. As such, it can be used as a reference document by all those involved in service strategy, development, purchasing, and delivery.

50   Part A gives a background to each of the three groups of disorder covered in the report; offers a synthesis of views on current service strengths and weaknesses, gleaned by the HAS review teams from service carers and users (elicited from HAS team visits to six districts in England and Wales); and looks at the efficacy of prevailing services for these client groups.

51   Chapter four gives some account of the nature of each of the three groups of conditions, including their definitions, causes and characteristics; their consequences and development; and the typical impact they have on health and social services, as well as carers, their friends and families. Chapter four also gives details about the known epidemiology of each of these disorders.

52   In chapter five, there is an account of the views of users and carers themselves, particularly highlighting the main problems that carers for each of these disorders commonly encounter. The discussion of their needs ranges from earlier and more accurate diagnosis, through rehabilitation and respite services, to requirements for more information and specialist advice.

53   Chapter six gives an account of the services for these patients in the six districts that the HAS review teams visited in the course of this thematic review. Their findings cover a diversity of local services, as well as voluntary organisations and the work of key clinicians and their teams. Alongside the problems and challenges they encountered, concerning, for example, identification and diagnosis, residential and respite care and domiciliary support, there are examples of good practice in each area. The chapter also covers the state of service development and commissioning, highlighting the key problems that appear to present obstacles to effective planning, commissioning and purchasing processes.

54   Part B presents a strategy for improving services in the future. Chapter seven summarises the principal concepts affecting service development and places these alongside a summary of the challenges facing service commissioners and providers. Chapter eight highlights the importance of establishing a strategic approach to commissioning and providing services, particularly given the relatively small number of patients concerned and the potential effectiveness of directing resources to them appropriately. That chapter provides key considerations for purchasing services for patients with each of the three disorders.

55   Part C provides commissioners and purchasers with information about generally well regarded commissioning and purchasing principles. Much of this information has been gleaned from several thematic reviews carried out by the HAS in recent years. Furthermore, the approach to commissioning and purchasing advocated here has been tested by the further work done by the HAS in advising many health and local authorities and key providers on the implementation of its advice formulated in previous reviews. While this report focuses on the needs of these three specific client groups, the emphasis is on the development of a general framework for commissioning and purchasing services for people with longer-term disorders. The chapter includes descriptions of idealised approaches to commissioning, as well as practical advice. Of particular relevance to the development of services for these patient groups are recommendations about contracting with non-statutory organisations. Chapter ten sets out the framework needed for an effective commissioning action plan.

56   Part D provides a number of topics that will be useful to commissioners, purchasers and providers in planning and delivering services for people with ABI, early onset dementia and HD. Chapter eleven deals with the critical legal issues such as consent to treatment,

detention of clients under the Mental Health Act 1983 and restraint procedures. Chapter twelve focuses on some of the principles of good practice in service delivery, including the importance of planning services from the users' and carers' viewpoints and building upon the best of existing service models. The chapter illustrates recommended practice through the cycle of treatment as it affects health and social services and the non-statutory agencies.

57   Chapter thirteen focuses on the important issues of training and appropriate staffing that are required to maintain and improve services. This covers training for people in general medical services as well as specialist services and looks at the long-term staffing requirements needed to cope with people whose brain disease or damage essentially requires long-term care, including acute, community and residential elements.

58   Part E focuses specifically on the way forward for providers of services for people with ABI, early onset dementia and HD. Chapter fourteen examines the clinical task facing professionals dealing with each of the disorders. Chapter fifteen is directed at the key areas for provider managers to take into account, such as the need for clinical leadership, the effectiveness of the CPA, the development of inpatient units, and developing alliances with specialist private sector providers and voluntary organisations.

59   Part F provides all those involved in the care of these patients with reference material. Chapter sixteen offers accessible checklists by reproducing tables and figures from the text that present the key factual information and recommendations. Chapter seventeen provides a bibliography and the full references to published works that are quoted in this report.

60   Finally, Annex A explains the origins and methodology of the review; Annex B provides definitions of the principal terms employed in the report, as well as recommended definitions of ABI, early onset dementia and HD; Annex C provides a fuller glossary of medical and scientific terms relevant to this report; Annex D describes the Glasgow Outcome Scale and the Glasgow Coma Scale that are used widely for evaluating individual cases of brain injury and lists other assessment needs; Annex E summarises key policy developments; and Annex F gives brief details about the editors, authors and service visitors involved in the review and in the preparation of this report.

The Background

*The Nature of Acquired
Brain Injury,
Early Onset Dementia
and Huntington's Disease*

INTRODUCTION

61   Acquired brain injury, early onset dementia and Huntington's Disease are a diverse range of disorders which present shared problems for commissioners and providers in the health and social services. This is because:

- people with these disorders constitute small but clearly-defined groups characterised by severe, and in some cases, progressive physical and psychological impairments that:

    - have profound impacts on all areas of life; and

    - require major and often long-term commitments from health and social care services;

- currently, many people with these disorders do not receive high quality health or social services, and are often placed in inappropriate types of care such as:

    - acute hospital wards (both medical and psychiatric);

    - nursing homes for elderly mentally ill people; and

    - private hospitals distant from friends and family;

- major improvements in services could be achieved in many districts by re-directing resources from high cost, but inappropriate, placements rather than by allocating additional revenue.

62   This chapter reviews the definitions, causes, and needs of people suffering forms of these three sorts of disorder in turn. It summarises knowledge on causes and needs, and then reviews the incidence (the number of new cases) and prevalence (the number of existing cases at any one time) of each.

ACQUIRED BRAIN INJURY

Definition and Causes

63   Acquired brain injury (here abbreviated to ABI) is defined as:

"An injury to the brain that has occurred since birth. It can be caused by an external physical force or by metabolic derangement. The term acquired brain injury includes traumatic brain injuries, such as open or closed head injuries, and non-traumatic brain injuries, such as those caused by strokes and other vascular accidents, tumours, infectious diseases, hypoxia, metabolic disorders (insulin shock, liver, and kidney disease), and toxic products taken into the body through inhalation or ingestion. The term does not include brain injuries that are congenital or produced by birth trauma." (adapted from the 1996 Standards Manual and Interpretive Guidelines for Medical Rehabilitation, the Rehabilitation Accreditation Commission (CARF) 1996).

64   Table 1 summarises the causes of ABI. The most common cause among people under the age of 65 years is direct violence (trauma), which results in the death of, or injury to, nerve cells and nerve fibres. Although traumatic brain injury (here abbreviated to TBI) is the most common cause of ABI, the brain can also be damaged by a variety of other processes. These include:

- haemorrhage, in which the brain is damaged by bleeding (stroke);

- severe reduction in the supply of oxygen to the brain (anoxia or hypoxia), which may result from drowning or choking;

- infections;

- toxins; and

- nutritional deficiency, which is often associated with alcohol misuse.

Table 1

Causes of Acquired Brain Injury	
Head Trauma	- Closed (the skull is not penetrated but the brain is shaken violently within the skull) - Open (the skull is penetrated)
Haemorrhage	- Around the brain (extra-dural, sub-arachnoid and sub-dural) - Inside the brain (intra-cerebral)
Metabolic	- Due to severely reduced supply of oxygen to the brain (hypoxia) - caused by, for example, choking, carbon monoxide poisoning, cardiac arrest or drowning - Due to severely reduced supply of glucose (which is essential for metabolism) to the brain - for example, caused by insulin overdosage
Nutritional	- Due to lack of essential vitamins (usually in the context of general self-neglect and often associated with alcohol misuse)
Infection	- Due to viruses such as Herpes Simplex and HIV (encephalitis) - Due to bacteria (meningitis and brain abscess) - Due to fungal and other infections (usually in people with HIV or on immuno-suppressant drugs)
Toxic	- Alcohol, heavy metals, such as lead and solvents
Other	- eg thrombosis blocking the blood supply to the brain.

65   Primary brain damage may set in train serious secondary events such as swelling of the brain tissue, and a cascade of chemical events within the brain, thereby causing the death of brain cells.

66   Irrespective of the cause of ABI, the pattern of subsequent deficits depends mainly on the severity and location(s) of the brain damage. A severe brain injury causes loss of consciousness (coma) followed by a further period of confusion and disorientation. In the case of TBI, the total period of disorientation is known as the period of post-traumatic amnesia (PTA). This is the period between the injury and the time when the subject subsequently regains continuous day-to-day memory. It includes any period spent in a coma. As a rule, the longer the period of PTA, the worse the recovery, and the duration of PTA can be used as an indicator of prognosis. This is summarised in Table 2.

Table 2

Severity of PTA and Outcome		
PTA	**Severity**	**Expected Outcome**
Up to 1 hr	Minor	Full recovery, although a small number of patients have prolonged and significant problems.
1 hr - 1 day	Moderate	Full recovery, but there may be problems (eg memorising and memory loss, irritability, emotional lability) for some months.
2 - 7 days	Severe	Eventually, most patients will make a full recovery, although this could take many weeks or months.
1 - 2 weeks	Very Severe	The chances of full recovery diminish with this severity of PTA. Recovery is likely to be slow (over many months), and often incomplete.
2 - 4 weeks	Extremely Severe	Greatly diminishing chances of full recovery.
> 4 weeks	Extremely Severe	Chances of complete recovery are extremely small. Most patients will have permanent and significant disabilities.

67   A more specific measure of coma is provided by the Glasgow Coma Scale (GCS). The scale is included in Annex D. The relationship between the GCS score, severity of coma and outcome is shown in Table 3.

Table 3

GCS Score Related to the Severity and Outcome from Brain Injury		
GCS	**Severity**	**Outcome**
3 - 5	Very Severe	High risk of death. Those who survive will have permanent and significant disabilities
6 - 8	Severe	Most patients will survive but with a high probability of permanent and significant problems
9 - 12	Moderate	Eventual complete recovery for most patients but this may take many months and even then there may be residual problems
13 - 15	Minor	Rapid and complete recovery for most patients. Nonetheless, a small number will have significant and prolonged problems

68   The location of damage to the brain has an important impact on the pattern of subsequent deficits. Figure 1 shows some diagrammatic views of areas and lobes of the brain that are mentioned below. Figure 1 also contains scans and photographs of the brain that give vital and anatomically correct pictures of brains to complement the labelled line diagrams. All of the illustrations in Figure 1 are of healthy brain anatomy and tissues.

Figure 1a

Side View of a Healthy Human Brain

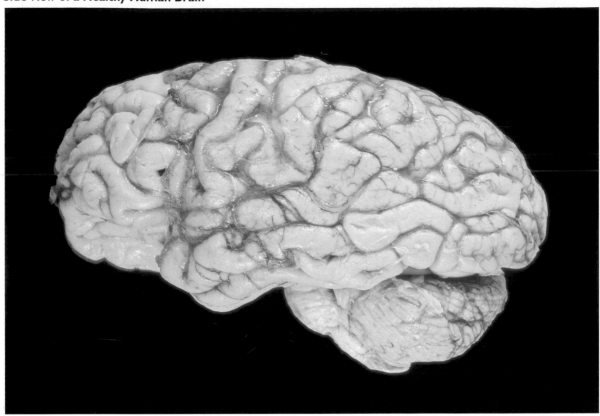

The Left Hemisphere of the Brain, Cerebellum and Brain Stem Viewed from the Left

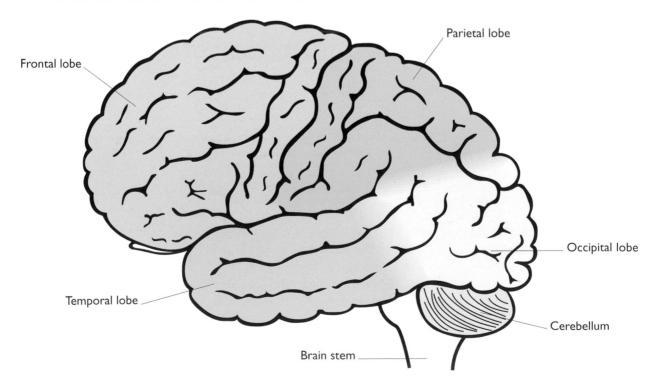

Figure 1b

Median (profile) Section through the Centre of a Whole Human Brain

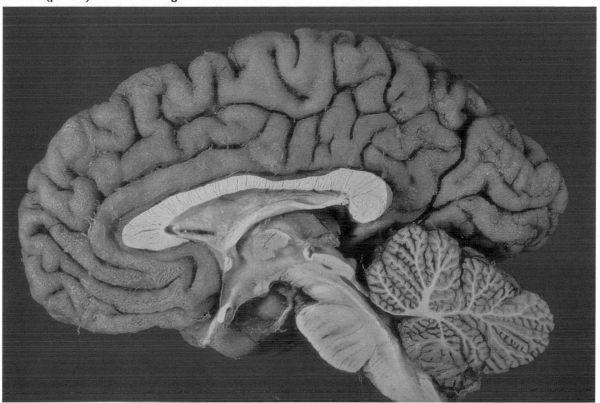

Internal Surface of the Right Hemisphere

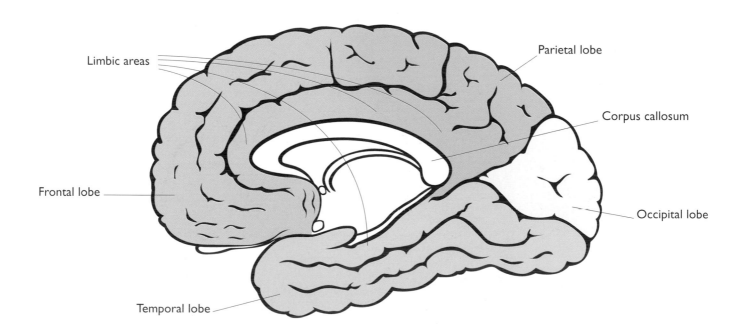

Figure 1c **False-colour Nuclear Magnetic Resonance (NMR) Image of an Axial Section through a Human Head showing a Normal Brain**

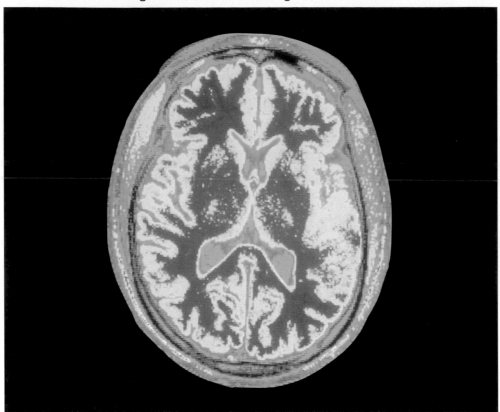

Figure 1d **The Brain Viewed from Below**

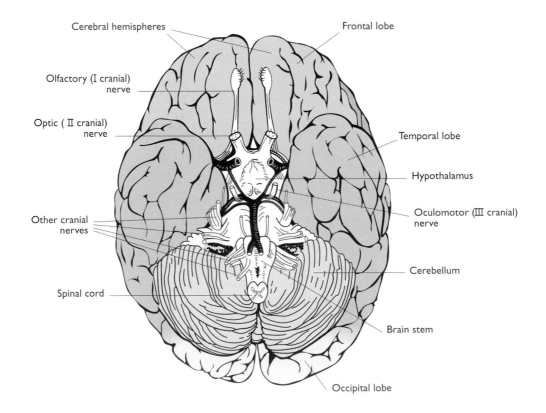

Figure 1e

**Coloured Magnetic Resonance Imaging (MRI) –
Median Sagittal Scan through a Human Head**

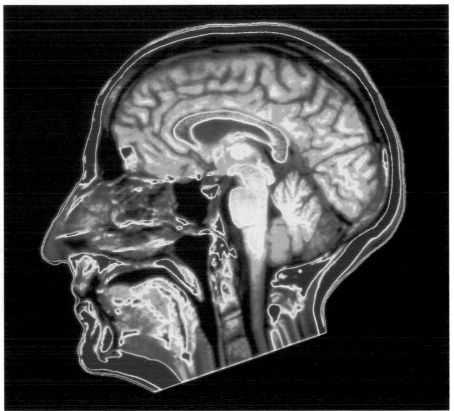

Diagram Indicating Some of the Structures Seen in the MRI Scan Above

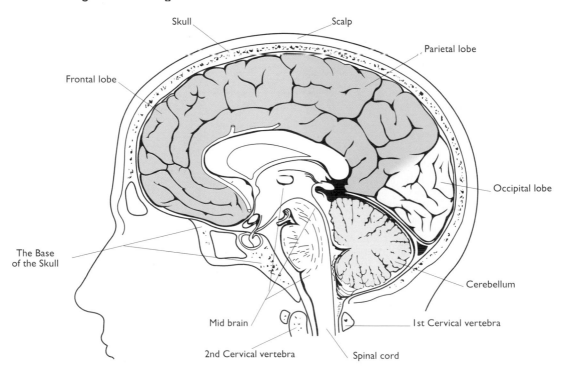

69   People with lesions in areas of the brain that are important in the control of behaviour will have significant deficits which cause major problems in daily life.

- For example, right-handed patients with damage to the left hemisphere of the brain may have disorders of language which compromise their abilities to plan and execute complex movements.

- Those with damage to the right hemisphere may have difficulty in making sense of visuo-spatial information, and in comprehending and communicating emotions.

- Damage to the frontal lobes leads to difficulty in expressing or inhibiting emotions, difficulties in initiation (`get up and go'), and difficulties in planning and problem-solving.

- Damage to the inner part of the temporal areas causes difficulties in inhibiting emotional reactions, and severe problems in learning and memory.

- Damage to the parietal areas causes complex spatial and language difficulties, and damage to the areas linking frontal, temporal, parietal and subcortical structures can lead to highly complex difficulties so that the injured person finds it difficult to recognise that he/she has deficits. Such a patient may deny that they have a weakness, or a cognitive or emotional problem.

Figures 2 and 3 opposite are scans that illustrate some of the focal aspects of brain injury. They should be compared and contrasted with the pictures of healthy brains in Figure 1.

Figure 2 shows the damage caused by a haemorrhage into one of the parietal lobes. It is the sort of focal injury that causes the symptoms and disabilities of stroke (eg muscular weakness and increased tone on the opposite side, possibly associated with loss of certain types of sensation).

Figure 3 shows a haemorrhage between the skull and the dura (one of the meninges – the tissues that cover the brain). In this case, injury to the head has probably caused damage to an artery resulting in a haemorrhage that can accumulate rapidly. The scan shows that the brain has not been invaded by the haemorrhage but that it has put pressure on one side, thereby distorting the anatomy and functioning, of the brain.

Figure 2 **Brain Haemorrhage (yellow area) due to Stroke**

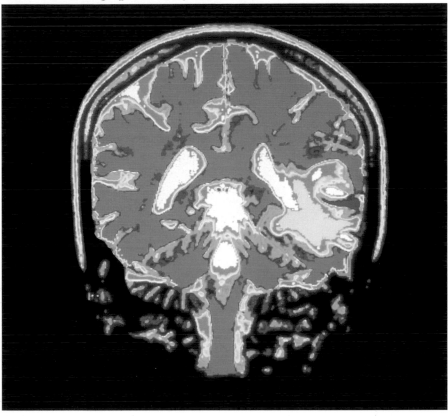

Figure 3 **Transverse Section of the Skull and the Brain**
showing a Recent Epidural Haemorrhage (red oval centre left)

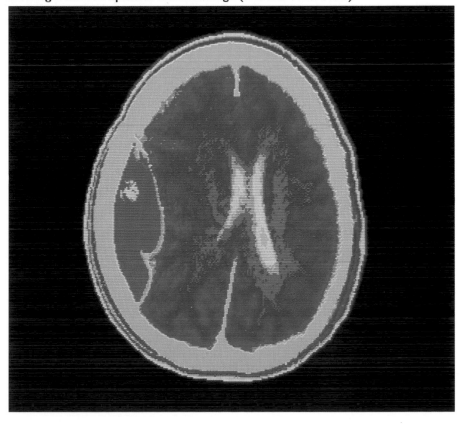

70   In practice, the assessment of ABI and of its subsequent deficits is much more complex than this simplified account suggests. All too often, brain damage is diffuse, patchy, and/or multi-focal, rather than neatly compartmentalised into impacts on discrete lobes or hemispheres. The pattern of deficits that results will also be affected by the state of the person's brain before injury, the nature of surgical and other clinical interventions, the extent of the patient's continuing abilities as well as disabilities, and the nature of the patient's environment. Thus, some patients with a PTA of many weeks have a good outcome, particularly when they have been intelligent and resilient before injury, and have strong family and environmental support. By contrast, a minor brain injury may lead to devastating handicap in a patient who, before injury, had acquired few of the complex skills necessary for survival in the community and whose environment after the injury is a poor one, which could foster disability and illness behaviour. Thus, the complexity of diagnosis makes it essential that every patient with ABI has a thorough and skilled evaluation by experienced clinicians that includes their physical status, but also extends well beyond it.

Long-Term Outcome

71   Severe ABI leaves a person with physical, cognitive, emotional and behavioural disabilities. The impacts of these are summarised here.

Physical Disability

72   The greater the severity and extent of brain damage, the more likely it is that a patient will have severe physical deficits, with consequences to their mobility, employment and quality of life. The main physical disabilities that occur are:

- limb weakness or paralysis;

- limb stiffness (spasticity);

- disturbed gait;

- impaired balance;

- sensory impairment;

- epilepsy.

73   Physical disabilities of this kind may be particularly severe after a stroke, but often there is a rapid rate of recovery after trauma. Sensory impairments are more common after stroke than after TBI. Clinicians who are inexperienced in assessing and managing people who have suffered ABI may cease treatment for some patients who have extremely severe traumatic injuries because there is no expectation of recovery. This can result in these patients acquiring additional physical deficits (particularly untreated limb contractures) if they begin to recover some years later. Such unnecessary excess disabilities can set very severe constraints on the resulting quality of life and can greatly inhibit cognitive and behavioural recovery (Denys et al, 1996).

Cognitive Disabilities

74   Impacts of brain injury on learning, memory, thinking, planning, perception and communication after ABI are frequent and often prolonged. In the period immediately after injury, these cognitive problems usually result from confusion, so that the patient's capacity to

process information is severely impaired. Patients with these disabilities may be:

- disorientated;

- unsure of where they are or why, or of what is happening; and

- very likely to misinterpret what goes on around them.

Emotional and Behavioural Disabilities

75   The emotional and behavioural problems that occur early after ABI may reflect gross confusion at that stage. In cases of this kind, the ability of an injured person to process information is only partially recovered and consequently he or she may misinterpret external events as threats. Occasionally, confusion of this kind may last for many months. Patients with this problem need to be managed in safe and predictable environments.

Psychiatric Disorders

76   There is an increased risk of major psychiatric disorders after ABI, particularly depression, anxiety disorders and psychoses. ABI also leads to a higher incidence of the side effects of medication and other complications in clinical management.

77   Brain injury can pose tremendous problems to injured people who are trying to pick-up their lives in the community. Friendships disappear, work may no longer be available and family life may be profoundly and negatively affected. After severe TBI, approximately 30% of patients return to work, although this may mean work in a lower position or a form of sheltered employment (Brooks et al, 1987). The best predictors of failure to return to work are:

- the severity of brain injury;

- the difficulty that an injured person has in recognising his or her deficits; and

- the presence of significant behaviour and cognitive impairment, most particularly:

    - anger;

    - poor social presentation; and

    - attention, communication, and memory impairment.

78   This confirms the more general observation that, in planning for a patient's return to their family, social and vocational life, the cognitive, emotional and behavioural deficits have the most serious day-to-day consequences. These deficits are the central target for treatment in the rehabilitation phase of management.

The Impact of ABI on Families and Carers

79   The changes in patients after ABI, particularly the changes in behaviour, have a profound effect on others around them. Early after the injury, friends and family rally around and are grateful for any small change in their relative or friend. But after this initial phase, friends often lose contact, and family members become forced in upon themselves and socially isolated. Then the burden on family members can become very high, and tends to increase over time. By the fifth year after a severe TBI,

between 60% and 70% of family members report high levels of emotional distress. This distress is not trivial; approximately 25% of relatives have clinically significant levels of anxiety or depression (Brooks, 1990). Furthermore, these problems are not often reported spontaneously by carers. So, any examination of a person after ABI must incorporate a separate interview with their partner and carers.

80   The reasons for the high levels of family distress are manifold, but two predominate. The first is the major role-shift forced on the (usually female) family member who cares for the injured patient; the second is the nature of the changes in the life of people after ABI.

81   Those who have the most severe (and unpleasant) emotional and behavioural changes are found to have family members who experience the highest level of burden. Not surprisingly, the changes in patients that predict high family burden also predict failure to return to work (irritability, anger, depression). Particularly in the case of more severe injury, high levels of family burden usually, but not always, result in:

   • divorce;

   • separation; and

   • the rupturing of long-term relationships.

82   Almost invariably, where relationships survive, the character of close relationships changes. All too often, the wife of an injured man becomes less of a friend, lover, and partner, and more of a minder and caregiver (Tate et al, 1989).

83   ABI places serious demands upon health, social, and voluntary and charitable services. The staff who provide services may be inexperienced in meeting the complex needs of people after an ABI, particularly when those needs are in respect of emotional and behavioural problems. Management of people with these problems is frequently made more difficult by:

   • the co-existing impairment of their cognitive functioning;

   • their inability to recognise that there are problems that require treatment; and

   • relative improvement in their behaviour making it more difficult for others to help.

84   After ABI, some people are referred to services as a consequence of behavioural impairments that are of such severity that they are unmanageable except with the help of specialist clinicians. In these circumstances, provision of local, skilled, flexible and experienced neuro-rehabilitation and neuropsychiatric teams can have a major positive impact but, as found in this review, patients in most parts of the country have limited access to teams with this level of integrated skills.

Children with Acquired Brain Injury

85   There is a common misconception among clinicians that children do well after ABI. This is not the case. The situation is also influenced by the circumstance of injury in that it occurs in young people whose brain function, behaviour and emotional capacity are relatively immature and in a period of rapid change and development. These processes add to and complicate the ways in which injury affects how young people

integrate new experiences and learning thereafter. Injury to an organ which functioning is maturing rapidly will necessarily produce interactive impacts on the processes of bio-psycho-social development that are central to growing up. Experience shows that young people have the same range of outcomes as adults and severe problems of cognitive development and behaviour are common after a severe brain injury.

86   These problems may result in major difficulties at school. Experience indicates that teachers and educational psychologists may believe that a child who is brain injured is being difficult (ie, they won't rather than can't achieve some task). After ABI, many children have special educational needs, yet the process of statementing may be long delayed. Due to inexperience and poor recognition of the impact of the injuries, the resulting statements may not reflect the full extent of the disabilities and resulting needs. Furthermore, as new life milestones and challenges are reached (changing schools, leaving school), injured children may experience and/or manifest new behaviour problems as the impact of the physical, psychological and emotional sequelae of the brain injury take on new meaning in the life of each young person and are revisited in their psycho-social development.

EARLY ONSET DEMENTIA

Definition and a Summary of the Causes

87   Dementia is a term that indicates a severe decline in a person's ability to think, remember and reason. It is formally defined by the World Health Organisation as: "*A syndrome due to disease of the brain, usually of a chronic or progressive nature, in which there is impairment of multiple, higher cortical functions, including memory, thinking, orientation, comprehension, calculation, learning capacity, language and judgement. Consciousness is not clouded. The cognitive impairments are commonly accompanied, and occasionally preceded, by deterioration in emotional control, social behaviour or motivation*" (World Health Organisation, 1992).

88   Dementia is caused by the death of brain cells in critical brain areas. This report considers the nature and particular impacts of dementia that arises in people who are younger than 65 years old at onset. Table 4 summarises the main causes of dementia in people below the age of 65 years. It is important to be aware that the most common causes for people in this age group, as in more elderly people, are degenerative brain diseases. There are many diseases of this kind and they are usually diagnosed by reference to the natural history of the dementing illness (how it develops and progresses over time). Nonetheless, in many instances, confirmation of the precise diagnosis may only be possible by a pathologist who examines the brain after the person has died.

Table 4

Causes of Dementia
Progressive Causes
- Alzheimer's Disease - Vascular (multiple infarction) - Pick's Disease and other lobar dementias - Lewy Body Disease - Huntington's Disease - Creutzfeldt-Jakob Disease (spongiform encephalopathy) - Infection (HIV, neurosyphilis) - Progressive supranuclear palsy - Wilson's Disease - Kuf's Disease - Demyelinating Disease
Dementia Due to Brain Damage
- Traumatic brain injury - Brain haemorrhage - Brain infection (meningitis and encephalitis) - Hypoxia and hypoglycaemia - Poisoning (lead and other heavy metals) - Alcohol misuse
Potentially Reversible Conditions that may Present as Dementia
- Hypothyroidism and other endocrine disorders - Drug toxicity - Liver and kidney failure (chronic) - Vitamin deficiencies (particularly B vitamins) - Hydrocephalus - Severe depression

89   The most common single cause of dementia in people under 65 years is Alzheimer's Disease. A more detailed clinical account of this condition and its impact upon the affected person and their family will be given here followed by briefer accounts of the other less common causes of dementia. While there are differences in clinical presentation across the different causes, all lead to global and severe impairment in daily living skills, emotional reactions and personality. Hence, the impacts upon family and other people who care for affected persons are similar and these are considered at the end of this section.

Alzheimer's Disease

Pathology and Genetics

90   Alzheimer was a German pathologist who, at the beginning of this century, described microscopic brain changes in people who had developed dementia. The most characteristic are a loss of normal neurons and the accumulation of abnormalities that are described as plaques and neurofibrillary tangles. These are illustrated by the pictures in Figure 4.

Figure 4 **The Anatomy of Alzheimer's Disease**

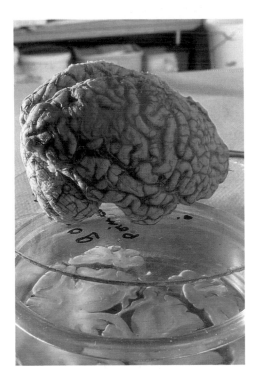

Figure 4a
**Post-mortem Specimen of
a Whole Brain from an
Alzheimer's Disease Victim**

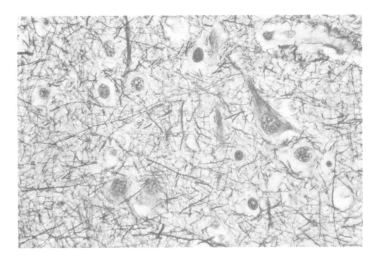

Figure 4b
**Light Micrograph of
Human Brain Tissue
in Alzheimer's Disease**

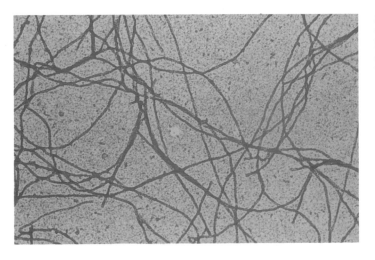

Figure 4c
**Coloured Transmission
Electron Micrograph (TEM)
through a Section of Brain
Tissue in Alzheimer's Disease**

91 Though the disease is most common in people over the age of 80, dementia of the Alzheimer type (DAT) can develop as early as 40 years of age. In a small proportion of people with Alzheimer's Disease the disorder runs in the family. The precise proportion of familial cases is disputed but includes early and late onset cases. Four separate chromosomes have so far been implicated, 1, 14, 19 and 21. The first to be discovered, and the commonest, is an abnormality in a gene on chromosome 21 which produces amyloid precursor protein (APP). It is not known how this leads to the disease in later life. When AD is familial it has an autosomal dominant transmission, that is to say each child of an affected parent has a 50% chance of inheriting the gene and everyone with the gene develops the disorder if they live long enough.

Clinical Features

92 Although there is some research that indicates that the initial clinical presentation of DAT may include a range of psychiatric symptoms, such as depression and paranoia, usually, the initial clinical presentation of DAT is one of worsening forgetfulness, often accompanied by emotional changes. There is a progressive worsening of memory which includes recall of day-to-day events, deterioration in the ability to recall names of familiar people and objects, and the ability to carry out tasks at which a person was previously competent. Early on, this leads to problems in coping with complex work-related tasks and progresses to include difficulties with the most basic domestic tasks (for example, how to turn on a radio or cooker, open a car, door etc). Eventually, the ability to communicate with words deteriorates until this skill is lost.

93 The most common emotional problems in the early stages are depression and anxiety which can sometimes be of clinical severity. Bouts of sudden tearfulness, laughter or anger can occur with little or no cause. There may be aggressive outbursts, sometimes without preceding anger or warning. Eventually, the condition deteriorates to a state in which there is absence of emotional expression and response.

94 In the earliest stages of the disease, a sufferer often has some awareness that a problem is developing. As the disease progresses this awareness, or insight, is lost and there is also a gradual loss of social skills. What this means is that an affected person does not appreciate the social setting they are in, or is not able to judge what behaviour is socially appropriate. This leads to embarrassment for family members and others and may lead to a restriction in social contacts for the person and for their family.

95 While it is possible to speak of early, middle and late stages of the disease, such staging is artificial as there is a seamless progression in most cases. The progression of the disease is characterised by a gradual loss of skills in every domain of life resulting in increasing dependence. The last skill to be lost is the ability to walk. Restlessness to the point of agitation is common and, when associated with severe cognitive impairment, can present major problems for carers as the affected person has no sense of danger or risk. Alterations in sleep pattern can occur, most commonly insomnia or frequent waking accompanied by wandering. Continence problems may begin with an inability to find or recognise the toilet, or to unzip or unbutton clothing. Later, there is loss of bladder and bowel control. The time course in which deterioration occurs is variable but is usually five to ten years from onset to the most severe disability.

Dementias in Down's Syndrome

96   Almost all adults with Down's syndrome who are over the age of 40
      develop the neuropathological changes of Alzheimer's Disease. The
      distribution of the Alzheimer-like changes in the brain is generally similar
      to that in non-learning disabled people. Age-specific prevalence rates of
      clinical dementia of 9.4% for the age range 40-49 years, and 56.1% for
      50-59 and 54.5% for 60-69 have been reported (Prasher, 1995). The
      mean age of onset of dementia is in the fifth decade of life, though
      dementia as early as 30 years has been reported. The clinical
      presentation is similar to that in people who do not have a learning
      disability. A genetic association between Alzheimer's Disease and
      Down's syndrome has been established with the gene coding for beta
      amyloid precursor protein (APP) located on chromosome 21.

Vascular Dementia

97   In vascular (or multi-infarct) dementia, there is progressive damage to
      brain tissue due to the occlusion of small arteries. This leads to multiple
      areas of damage which can occur in any part of the brain. The clinical
      picture may be similar to that seen in Alzheimer's Disease in which
      there is extensive cell death in the cortex of the brain. Where
      subcortical damage predominates, the picture is more one of
      progressive slowing of thought and impairment of reasoning associated
      with blunting of emotion and motivation. Vascular dementia may be
      suspected when a person is known to have vascular disease (a history
      of stroke, myocardial infarction or hypertension) and a step-wise
      progression of the dementing disease, ie there are relatively abrupt
      changes in function or loss of skills.

Lewy Body Dementia

98   Lewy bodies are microscopic brain abnormalities. They were first found
      in people with Parkinson's Disease but since then, they have been
      found in people where there is an absence of this disease. The clinical
      features of dementia can include both skill loss and slowing of thought
      processes. A number of other symptoms are also reported, including
      hallucinations and fluctuations in cognitive function (McKeith et al,
      1992).

Pick's Disease and Other Dementias Due to Focal Degeneration

99   The diseases described so far involve pathological changes in many
      parts of the brain. However, it is possible to develop dementia due to
      degeneration of one lobe or area of the brain, usually the fronto-
      temporal or parietal areas. Pick was the first to describe such a
      dementia which now bears his name.

100   In this disease, balloon-like cells develop and normal cell populations
      reduce in number in the affected areas of the brain.

101   In dementia due to frontal lobe degeneration, the earliest features are
      characteristic. They are:

      •   personality changes;

      •   emotional blunting or fatuousness;

      •   social disinhibition;

      •   impaired drive and goal-directed behaviour;

- restlessness; and

- impairment in reasoning.

Generally, affected individuals have no awareness of these problems or insight into their implications. As the disease progresses over several years, a global impairment in daily living skills accrues, together with severe emotional blunting. Restlessness turns into apathy and inactivity. Pick's disease is familial in about 10% of cases.

Creutzfeldt-Jakob Disease (CJD)

102   CJD is a form of human spongiform encephalopathy – a degenerative brain disease with characteristic microscopic sponge-like changes in the brain. The incidence is approximately 1 per million of the population per year. The clinical features include:

- deteriorating memory and other cognitive functions;

- inco-ordination;

- rigidity;

- muscle jerks; and

- visual impairment.

Usually, the disease shows clinically in the 6th and 7th decades of life and leads to death within six months of onset, in most cases. 10% of cases are familial but most cases are believed to be due to sporadic genetic mutation. The disease is caused by an abnormal protein (PrPp). Earlier onset cases have been linked to the administration of growth hormone from a donor with CJD. A series of 10 early onset cases has recently been reported by the CJD Surveillance Unit raising concern over the possibility of transmission of the bovine form of spongiform encephalopathy to humans before measures to exclude infected offal were introduced in 1989. A link is not yet proven (Brown, 1996).

103   Most people who develop CJD are managed by neurological, geriatric and psychogeriatric services. Their rapid progression to physical disability and death means that their care needs are usually met by health rather than social services.

Huntington's Disease

104   Dementia tends to occur in the later stages of Huntington's Disease, and this is described later in this chapter.

HIV and Other Infections

105   Dementia occurs in the late stages of HIV/AIDS and can be caused by the HIV or brain infection by other organisms to which the affected person becomes susceptible by virtue of their impaired immune response. The dementia in AIDS is generally characterised by cognitive slowing and reduced drive and these features are due to progressive damage to subcortical brain structures (Maj, 1990). In the UK, this is generally seen as a near-terminal event and occurs at a time when there are other life-threatening infections.

106   Neurosyphillis is now rare but, in its later stages, produces a progressive dementia.

Other Causes

107 Any disorder which involves the destruction or degeneration of widespread or cognitively critical areas of the brain can cause dementia. Hence, the following survey of other causes is not comprehensive. The earliest onset dementias (in children, adolescents and young adults) are caused by the metabolic, storage and related diseases which involve inherited deficiencies of important enzymes or other chemicals. In Wilson's Disease, copper deposits develop in the brain; in Kuf's Disease, lipfuscin is deposited. Dementia can occur in the later stages of multiple sclerosis. Progressive supranuclear palsy is a disease with a wide range of neurological symptoms including dementia characterised by slowing of thought and emotional blunting. It is mainly seen in elderly people.

108 Brain cell death may be brought about by direct insult, such as that caused by trauma, infection or prolonged alcohol misuse. Usually, the quantity of brain tissue damaged by these processes is not sufficient to result in dementia. Where the level of cognitive impairment is sufficient to warrant the term dementia, the level of care needed is necessarily high. However, in most cases, the dementia is not progressive and so this level of care may be needed over many years.

109 Some forms of dementia are caused not by the death of brain cells but by the slow, progressive development of widespread malfunctioning of brain cells. In some circumstances, this process may be reversible. Causes of this kind occur in around 10% of people who develop dementia when they are under the age of 65 years. In addition, a number of medical conditions (such as heart, kidney or liver failure, depression, and drug side-effects) may increase the level of disability in the early stages of a dementing illness.

Medical Interventions and Long-term Outcome

110 After initial assessment and investigation, a range of medical interventions may be beneficial and these are best delivered within a wider multi-disciplinary care programme. There is a need to maintain good general health (freedom from infections, adequate nutrition, protection of skin pressure areas, etc) as other medical problems can increase the level of disability of affected people. Where early onset Alzheimer's Disease runs in the family, referral to a department of medical genetics is important.

111 In the early stages, sufferers may develop clinical depression or an anxiety state which respond to antidepressant or anxiolytic medication. Aggression, sleep disturbance and restlessness are the greatest burdens for carers but are usually amenable to medical treatment. This may require the prescription of major tranquillisers. Supervision and review by specialist practitioners is particularly important in this context because idiosyncratic responses and side-effects to the psychotropic medication are common in this client group.

112 In general, the best approach is one that involves using a single drug, where possible, at the minimum effective dose. Currently, there is no means of slowing the progression of dementias of degenerative origin. Drugs which slow the breakdown of the neurochemical acetylcholine have been shown to produce short-term improvement in memory in the early stages of Alzheimer's Disease, but severe side-effects have limited their use to clinical trials (Dayer and Woodhouse, 1993).

113   In all forms of dementia, there is a progressive reduction in independence. One way of viewing the process is to consider that it is a reverse of what happens in human development. This is particularly evident in Alzheimer's Disease in which an averbal, but ambulant state progresses into a child-like, non-ambulant dependency. Each stage presents challenges and new forms of distress for carers and other family members (Sperlinger and Furst, 1994).

The Impact on Families and Carers

114   The development of dementia has a devastating effect upon each person's family and loved ones. Grief is accompanied by the need to adjust to an ever-changing caring role which requires the acquisition of new skills. There is a constant need for vigilance because of the changed behaviour and judgement of sufferers, including wandering and lack of awareness of risk, often at a time of disturbed sleep. Carers have differing needs dependent upon a variety of factors, including the level of support from their families and friends and their own emotional reactions. When dementia develops in the late 40s or early 50s, there may still be children at home, or they may have left and have young children themselves. These factors can be helpful or add to the pressures on carers.

Support Services

115   In most cases, a range of supports are needed including care at home (dressing, bathing, sitting services), daycare, respite and crisis care. In the terminal stages, which can persist for many years, there is a need for round-the-clock nursing care which is difficult to provide in a person's home. Care and support for the carers themselves are important. Much support and advice can be obtained from voluntary agencies, such as the Alzheimer's Disease Society and carers' groups. Professional support is also valued and needed and some services, such as the Admiral Nurse Project, have specifically targeted carers' needs (Greenwood and Walsh, 1995).

HUNTINGTON'S DISEASE

Definition and Characteristics

116   Huntington's Disease (HD) is an inherited progressive, irreversible degenerative disease of the nervous system. Its most characteristic feature is chorea, indeed the disease was known as Huntington's Chorea until recently. This term describes jerky, random, involuntary movements that disrupt normal actions. At first, chorea may appear to be fidgetiness, and therefore HD may not be recognised for years after its true onset. Gradually, these movements become more noticeable and incapacitating and more widespread, affecting the limbs, trunk, face and eyes. Surprisingly, the person suffering chorea may not be aware of the abnormal movements which are obvious to everyone else. Commonly, sufferers may also experience problems in co-ordinating their fine movements and in walking. Like the chorea, these problems may be minor at first and gradually worsen as the disease progresses.

117   Eventually, an affected person will need help with more and more aspects of his or her life and, ultimately, he or she will become totally dependent on the help of others. People who suffer HD develop:

- slowing of their voluntary movements;

- incontinence;

- unclear speech; and

- difficulty in swallowing that can lead to the risk of choking.

Their speech becomes thickened and unclear because of inco-
ordination of the muscles of the face, mouth, throat and upper body
and their ability to communicate is increasingly impaired. The amount of
energy used by sufferers in their involuntary movements and the
difficulties that they may experience in eating, can combine to make
weight loss a major problem. So, individuals who are severely affected
are advised to take 4,000 to 5,000 calories each day and usually this
involves providing them with dietary supplements.

118 Probably, all sufferers of HD have some degree of impaired intellectual
functioning but this may not be recognised in the earlier stages.
Memory, particularly recall, can be affected early in Huntington's
Disease, leading to profound disabilities in everyday living and an
increasing reliance on others. The cognitive impairment is of a
subcortical type (ie, it involves forgetfulness, slowing of thought
processes, apathy and impairment of the ability to manipulate
information) and it worsens as the disease progresses. Intellectual
impairment often affects the ability of sufferers to think ahead or
organise plans, and this is particularly disabling in everyday life.
Eventually, these impairments become severe enough to be
recognisable as a form of dementia, though there may have been
marked problems before this. This also explains why surveys that look
only at the incidence of dementia in Huntington's Disease
underestimate the magnitude and frequency of less severe intellectual
problems.

119 Approximately 50% of people with Huntington's Disease exhibit
changes in behaviour to the degree that they give rise to problems. In
decreasing order of frequency, the most common problematic
behaviour changes are:

- aggression and violence;

- suspiciousness; and

- poor temper control.

120 These changes in personality are caused by the physical brain
degeneration and are potentially treatable. Unfortunately, they are
often not recognised for what they are, either by families or by the
professionals involved.

Psychiatric Disorders in People Who Have Huntington's Disease

121 Frequently, people with HD develop psychiatric symptoms that are
underestimated and unrecognised. Watt and Seller (1993) reviewed
seven surveys of HD conducted between 1925 and 1986 which
estimated that the rates for depression and/or psychosis were between
21% and 56% and, for personality and behavioural disorders, the rates
were between 24% and 70%. This variation in results can be explained
by the use of different definitions of the psychiatric disorders and the
different stages reached by the subjects of the various recorded studies
in the progression of HD.

122   In practice, the usual methods to classify psychiatric illnesses, such as ICD 10 or DSM IV, are not easily applied to organic conditions. With that reservation in mind, many attempts have been made to measure the incidence and prevalence of a range of psychiatric conditions that occur in people who have Huntington's Disease. The following sections offer a summary.

Depression

123   Major depression occurs in about 30% of people who have HD (compared with 5% of the general population). Minor depression has a similar prevalence. Depression is difficult to recognise in people who have more advanced symptoms stemming from Huntington's Disease. It is all too easy to assume that early on in HD depression is justified or understandable. Consequently, depressed people who have HD may fail to receive the assessment and treatment they need.

Schizophrenia

124   Estimating the prevalence of schizophrenia, and comparison of the results from a range of studies, is complicated by the changes that have taken place in clinical practice and to the criteria for diagnosis of schizophrenia over the last 30 years. Consequently, there is no agreed figure for the incidence of schizophrenia in people who have HD, but symptoms of psychosis that are not sufficient to generate a diagnosis of schizophrenia may be seen in up to 10% of sufferers of HD.

Alcohol Misuse

125   The scientific literature reports both an increase and a prevalence of alcohol misuse that is similar to the general population. King (1985) has conducted the most thorough study of alcoholism in people who have HD and showed that the presence of HD did not increase risk of alcoholism in affected people.

Suicide

126   According to published research, the suicide rate in people who have HD ranges from 0.5% to 12.7% of all deaths. However, research has yet to indicate the proportion of those people with HD who have committed suicide while also suffering from mental illness.

The Onset of Psychiatric Disorders

127   Usually, the onset of minor depression and of behaviour and personality disorders occurs at around the time of the onset of the overt symptoms of HD. In 50%, it is the first sign of HD. Also research indicates that major depression and schizophrenia can occur throughout the course of Huntington's Disease, that is before, during, and after the onset of the physical symptoms and signs.

The Age of Onset and the Progression of Huntington's Disease

128   The average age of onset of the overt symptoms and signs of HD (usually defined by the beginning of physical symptoms) is the late thirties or forties. Nonetheless, the clinical phase of the disease can begin at any age and has been reported in children as young as four, as well as in people in their seventies. The age of onset can vary even within a family, and it is almost impossible to predict when symptoms will start in an individual. In about 5% of cases, the onset of HD is in childhood.

129   The time from onset to death is usually said to be about 15 to 17 years. However, this depends on many factors. Huntington's Disease is now being diagnosed at an earlier stage, and the management of the complications is improving. HD is not a disease that causes death directly, but people who have it become increasingly disabled and ultimately it is the complications of the disease that lead to death. There is some evidence that if the symptoms are identified earlier and managed better, the outlook will change.

130   At present, there is no treatment that alters the age of onset or the progression of HD. There are treatments for the symptoms but most professionals will not gain experience and expertise in managing HD as a consequence of its relative rarity.

Genetics

131   Huntington's is a genetically inherited disease. The gene was found in 1993, is named IT15 and lies on chromosome 4.

132   Huntington's Disease is a dominant condition and this means that if only one of the two copies of the gene that are ordinarily present in all humans is faulty, the person will develop the disease. Each time a person with the faulty gene has a child, she will pass on one copy of the IT15 gene, which may or may not be a copy of the faulty gene. This means that each child has a 50% chance of developing HD. It does not mean that half of the children in a family will have HD, as is sometimes thought. To put this another way, the risk to each future child of an HD sufferer is a 50% chance of inheriting the disorder. Therefore, all the children in each family, a proportion, or none of them, could inherit the disease. The gender of the child makes no difference to the risk since Huntington's Disease affects men and women equally.

133   If a person has the faulty gene, then they will show symptoms of the disease if they live long enough. Because HD usually does not develop until mid-life, people may die for other reasons before they show signs of the disease. But they may have had children by this time and passed on the gene, and the child may then develop HD in due course. Thus the disease may appear to skip a generation, or there may seem to be no family history. The other major reason for a lack of a family history in a particular case is non-paternity. That is neither the mother nor her husband have HD but the mother's husband is not the natural father of the affected individual and the natural father does have HD.

134   Because people have the genetic fault from the moment of conception, even though they do not show the disease until later in life, an analysis of their DNA will provide a predictive test.

135   When the IT15 gene is normal, it has a region where a sequence of three bases (the building blocks of DNA) is repeated. This is termed a triplet repeat. All normal individuals have this repeat sequence, and the actual number of repeats is inherited. In the case of HD, the number of repeats is higher (known as an expansion). Normal individuals have approximately 10 to 30 repeats and patients who have HD have 38 or more. The exact cut-off point for the disease has not yet been determined confidently, and the clinical significance for individuals who occupy the intermediate range has not been established yet. But this expansion of the triplet repeat is characteristic of HD and, although similar repeats may be seen in other conditions, it has always been

found in people with HD. This makes gene analysis, especially when coupled with a family history, a diagnostic test when HD is suspected.

136 If it can be shown that a person carries the expansion, then it is certain that they will go on to develop HD, although the age of onset or the progress of the disease cannot be predicted in individual cases. Also the gene test can be used to help people to plan their families. If a person knows that they carry the faulty gene, either because they have the clinical features of HD or have had a positive result from the predictive test, then a similar test can be carried out on their foetus in utero and early in pregnancy to see whether the unborn child has inherited the faulty gene or not. The possibility of terminating pregnancies when the gene fault is found in unborn children means that the capacity exists to assure parents that they will not pass the gene on to their children, provided they are willing and able to undergo the test and a termination.

137 Plainly, the genetics of this disease and the availability of a predictive test of this kind present those people who have the faulty gene and their professional advisers with challenging ethical dilemmas. While predictive testing is relatively simple in molecular genetic terms, it is much more complicated in emotional and ethical terms. Therefore, testing is only carried out in established centres of genetic excellence and the test is not available without appropriate counselling and support.

The Impact on Families and Carers

138 The changes in personality which may occur in people who have HD are very distressing to their families. In clinical practice, partners frequently describe the way in which they feel they have ended up married to a different person and, in all probability, not the sort of person they would have chosen. Feelings of regret and anger are very common responses and frequently marriages come under extreme strain.

139 The strain on the members of the families of people with HD is intensified by the impact of the implications stemming from the inherited nature of the disease and, more recently, by the availability of the predictive test to identify offspring who are at risk of developing the disease. Often, those who are at risk are involved in the care of their parents or other members of the family, and are constantly reminded of the reality of HD. It is not uncommon for a person to nurse their parent, then an older brother or sister and then, finally, succumb to the disease themselves, while worrying all the time that they have transmitted it to their children. Minor depressive illness is seen in about 25% of individuals who are at risk and is associated with these sorts of stresses. Nonetheless, research confirms that people at risk do not have a significantly increased prevalence of major depression or schizophrenia and this is surprising, given the observation of the pre-choreic onset of both these conditions.

140 People who have HD, and their families, require a range of services over time.

- When the diagnosis is made, there is a need for genetic testing, advice and counselling. Those relatives who are at risk, known gene-carriers and any relatives who show early signs of HD, should be offered follow-up support by a specialist who is familiar with the disease (be it a neurologist, neuropsychiatrist or psychiatrist) so that treatable symptoms are identified and dealt with appropriately.

- As the disease progresses, other professionals (social workers, occupational therapists, community psychiatric nurses and speech therapists) should become involved in order that families receive a comprehensive assessment of their needs.

- Inpatient assessment becomes important later but should be conducted in collaboration with the staff who provide support at home.

- Daycare and periodic respite allow patients to remain at home for longer but, often, this is offered inappropriately in services for elderly people.

- Finally, there is a need for terminal care when the needs of a sufferer for skilled nursing exceed the ability of the family to provide this.

Huntington's Disease in Childhood and Adolescence

141 Approximately 5% of people who have HD begin to show signs of the disease when they are children. About 90% of early onset cases of HD (ie before the age of 20) will have inherited the gene from their father. The triplet repeat region is unstable and the process of packaging chromosomes into sperm cells may encourage expansion. Statistics show that those people who inherit HD from their fathers have an earlier age of onset of symptoms and signs of the disease than those who inherit it from their mothers. Research indicates that very early presentation is associated with a large expansion of the triplet repeat and that this is likely to be associated with paternal transmission.

142 In rare cases, a child may develop symptoms and signs of the disease before their parent has been diagnosed.

143 Additionally, onset in childhood may be associated with a more aggressive and rapidly progressive form of the disease. When the onset of symptoms and signs occurs in childhood or adolescence, life expectancy is approximately the same as cases in which the onset is later, but the symptom complex is different from that seen when the onset is in adulthood. The differences include:

- less chorea;

- more rigidity associated with bradykinesis;

- a higher incidence of cerebellar signs and seizures; and

- a more rapidly evolving dementia.

These are typical features in juvenile onset cases and can delay the diagnosis, particularly when the family history is not known.

144 Predictive testing is not offered to people under the age of 18, but counselling is available, and diagnostic DNA analysis can be used in the doubtful cases that occur in childhood or adolescence.

EPIDEMIOLOGY

Acquired Brain Injury

145 There is no reliable information on the total number of new cases each
year of ABI, or of the number of people in the UK who are living with
the long-term consequences of brain damage either in themselves or in
a close relative or friend. Some data is available with respect to TBI, for
which the number of new cases each year with brain damage is
estimated to be approximately 250 for each 100,000 of the general
population. Of these, approximately 10 cases have severe injuries and
they are left with significant and permanent disability (Medical Disability
Society, 1988). Some less severe injuries also lead to permanent
disabilities.

146 Statistically, the typical patient who has suffered TBI:

- is young - between 15 and 30 years of age;

- is male;

- shows other evidence of risk-taking in their background; and

- has consumed alcohol in the period before the trauma.

Usually, their life expectancy is unaffected by the TBI, so the typical
patient may live a further 40 or 50 years after their initial trauma.

147 The next most common cause of ABI is stroke. The incidence of this
disorder is strongly linked to age, but about 28% of all strokes occur in
people under the age of 65 years (Gururaj et al, 1995). One survey
found 47 new cases of stroke each year among adults between the ages
of 35 and 64 years of age for each 100,000 of the general population
(Thorvaldson et al, 1995). The survival rate for stroke is less than that
for TBI, and about half of those who survive have significant and
continuing disabilities.

148 Few, if any, estimates of annual incidence are available for the remaining
causes of ABI (eg infection, toxins etc).

Early Onset Dementia

149 To date, the best estimate of the prevalence of dementia in people aged
between 45 and 64 years (Newens et al, 1993) is 34.6 per 100,000
people in this age range for Dementia of the Alzheimer Type (DAT), and
an additional 23.0 per 100,000 people in this age range for other
degenerative dementias. This gives a total of approximately 58 people
with all types of dementia for every 100,000 of the population aged
between 45 and 64 years. These figures are consistent with those from
research in other countries.

150 Note that degenerative dementia can develop below the age of 45
years, while dementia from severe single or multiple insults can develop
at any age. One community survey found that about 10% of people
with degenerative dementia under the age of 65 were aged under 45.

151 Dementia due to brain damage (from severe or multiple insults) can
arise at any age. No reliable data exists on the prevalence of dementia
due to brain damage. However, surveys of attenders at memory clinics
and residential home populations indicate that up to one third of
people under 65 with dementia have brain damage rather than
degeneration, alcohol being the most common damaging agent.

152   The best current estimate of the prevalence of degenerative dementia
       in people under 65 years is 15 per total population of 100,000 (based
       on a norm of 23% of the total population being aged between 45 and
       64 years). In the same population, approximately 5 people under 65
       years will suffer dementia due to brain damage. These are conservative
       estimates.

Huntington's Disease

153   Estimates of prevalence in the UK vary between 25-100 cases per
       million people (Harper, 1991). There is evidence that the higher
       prevalence rates are identified by the better and more comprehensive
       surveys. The generally accepted prevalence rate is between 50 and 100
       per million, and the Huntington's Disease Association estimates that
       there are 6,000 affected individuals in the UK.

Summary

154   Tables 5, 6 and 7 summarise the demands on local statutory health and
       social services commissioners by presenting the epidemiological data
       for a hypothetical health authority and its associated local authorities,
       that are responsible for a population of 500,000 people which has the
       national average prevalence of the disorders that are the subject of this
       report. These tables are derived from the approximate incidences and
       prevalences of the various disorders that are quoted in this report.

Table 5

The Prevalence of Disability after Acquired Brain Injury (estimated for a 500,000 total population)		
Disorder	**Prevalence**	**Remarks**
TBI	625	Survivors after severe head injury with significant permanent disability
Stroke	235	People aged 35-64 inclusive

Table 6

The Prevalence of Dementia in Younger People and Huntington's Disease (estimated for a 500,000 total population)		
Disorder	**Prevalence**	**Remarks**
Dementia • DAT	40	People aged 45- 64 years inclusive
• other degenerative dementias	26	People aged 45- 64 years inclusive
	7	People aged <45 years (estimated)
• due to brain damage	25	People aged < 65 years (estimated)
Huntington's Disease	50	Rates increase with the quality of the survey and this is the highest suggested prevalence

155 It should be emphasised that the three groups of disorders that are the subject of this report are part of a wider spectrum of brain disorders that are recognised as frequently giving rise to psychiatric disorders as complications. For comparison purposes, Table 7 shows the prevalence rates of other neurological conditions that also have psychiatric implications in an average health district with a population of 500,000 people.

Table 7

The Prevalence Rates of other Neurological Conditions that have Psychiatric Implications (estimated for a 500,000 total population)	
Condition	Rate
Parkinson's disease (idiopathic)	500
Multiple sclerosis	500
Epilepsy	2,500

156 The importance of this information is that it highlights the requirements of people with a wide range of brain injury and disease for services of the kind that are described in this report, on the basis of considering three particular client groups. The reasons for choosing these groups of exemplars of need have been highlighted in chapters 1, 2 and at the beginning of this chapter. Cumulatively, the prevalence of people with brain disease or injury of all types is higher than many people recognise.

CHAPTER 5

*Service Users' and
Carers' Views*

are a member, are often cited by carers as the resources most able to assist them in these circumstances.

199 At later stages of dementia, carers need regular help at home with everyday tasks. Home care support to this group of people requires a combination of knowledge, skills and continuity of relationships and input. Frequently, carers observe that there is less continuity of staff and that standards, such as that of good timekeeping, are met less well.

Respite Care

200 Specialist daycare services, that are organised on a flexible basis, are much needed by younger people with dementia in order to allow their carers to continue to work. The relative fitness, energy and physical strength of younger people with dementia make special demands on the range of respite that may be offered. Ideally, these services should be tailored specifically to the needs and circumstances of younger people with dementia.

201 In one HAS visit, carers described travelling daycare and carer support services that had been commissioned and funded by the social services department and provided by the Alzheimer's Disease Society. Although this was intended mainly for older people with dementia, nevertheless it was also supporting several younger people with dementia and their carers. The flexibility and responsiveness of this service was impressive.

Residential Respite and Continuing Care

202 Frequently, carers reported that the only residential respite care they had been offered was that in a home for older people with dementia or in an acute psychiatric unit. Facilities of these kind are distressing to relatives and to themselves. Residential respite care for younger people with dementia could be located on the same site as specialist day care and the establishment of continuing care for these people could also be developed as part of a specialist resource unit.

203 In 1994, the Alzheimer's Disease Society surveyed its 180 branches about local service provision for younger people with dementia and their carers. Key findings included:

- 87% of branches reported that the statutory authorities had not carried out any investigation into the needs and numbers of people in this client group;

- 94% of branches said specialist residential care was not available in their area;

- 72% of branches said that their health authority did not have a consultant who was identified for younger people with dementia;

- Only 13% of branches said specialist daycare or respite was available and only 15% said specialist home helps were available;

- 22% of branches were aware of genetic counselling services.

Summary

204 The key factor in meeting the needs of younger people with dementia and their carers is flexibility. Needs should be established both by considering the profiles of local populations (as in NHS needs assessments) and by the appropriate assessment of each individual, their situation and the services required and those provided in negotiation

with the younger person with dementia and their carers (as in assessments conducted by local authority staff). Often, carers require support to continue to meet their own needs for employment and social activities. Carers may wish to accompany the person they care for to day care or on holiday. They may also gain support and companionship from others in similar circumstances where they are free to be themselves (Cox and McClennan, 1994).

CHAPTER 6

*Service Commissioning
and Provision –
The Current Position*

evidence from the fieldwork suggests that if effective liaison does not occur within an agency, there is little prospect of it existing between agencies.

Disability Masking

247 Both the statutory health and social services may categorise acquired brain injury and Huntington's Disease as physical disorders, and this can result in failure to identify and treat any associated cognitive or behavioural disorders. Therefore, treatment of the mental health and cognitive consequences of these disorders may be ignored because the focus of clinical activity is dominated by concentration on restoring the loss of physical function. One social services department had a particularly rigid division between services for people who have physical disability and those who are mentally ill and this appeared to make it difficult for senior officers to recognise that a single client might have a combination of these problems.

Good Practice in Identification and Diagnosis

248 The visiting teams identified several examples of good practice in respect of the processes of identification and diagnosis.

- Some local branches of Headway have arranged for information packs about acquired brain injury and local services to be available in orthopaedic hospital wards. Headway and the other main charities have also circulated information packs to GPs and to other key agencies.

- One neuro-behavioural service has built links with the local charities that provide services for homeless people, because the staff recognise the high prevalence of brain injury in this population.

- In one district, a neuropsychiatrist is working alongside the supra-district genetics service to provide counselling for patients who have been diagnosed as having HD and their families, as well as providing basic genetic counselling.

Behaviour Management

Facilities for Inpatients

249 Five of the districts have specialised psychiatric inpatient facilities to which patients with acquired brain injury, Huntington's Disease and/or early onset dementia may be admitted. Most were self-contained units on a site shared with other psychiatric facilities, although one district had a new unit in a large village located between major urban centres. Most of the units were organised as a series of small wards, each of which specialised in a particular group of patients.

250 However, the visiting teams found no standard model of inpatient care, and there was considerable variation between different districts in categories of patients admitted, treatment programmes and criteria for discharge.

251 In the absence of specialised units of this kind, patients with acquired brain injury, early onset dementia or Huntington's Disease are admitted to a diverse range of local facilities including general psychiatric beds and beds for older people with psychiatric disorder. These were viewed as unsatisfactory options in most districts because the patient mix was

often inappropriate and could exacerbate problems in care planning for discharge as ward-attached staff, including social workers, lacked specialist knowledge of the conditions.

252   Also, many family carers oppose admission to psychiatric facilities because of the implication that the service user is mentally ill. An alternative is to admit patients to one of the non-NHS hospitals as an extra-contractual referral (ECR). This is seen by some commissioners as an unsatisfactory approach because of the high prices charged by these agencies and because admission removes patients from their home area.

Outreach Services

253   Most specialist psychiatric services have a strong inpatient focus, and they have limited outreach services, other than outpatient clinics. As a result, most specialist services probably have a minimal impact on services and people who live in health districts outside their immediate vicinity. A further consequence is that clinical resources are directed towards a small number of inpatients, many of whom run an inappropriate risk of becoming long-stay residents because of the lack of appropriate accommodation offering continuing care.

Examples of Good Practice

254   Examples of good practice include:

- In one district, a service for people with early onset dementia that had begun with the provision of a specialist community team rather than developing from an inpatient service. Access to inpatient beds in psychiatric and psychogeriatric services is negotiated on a case-by-case basis, using whichever inpatient facility is judged most appropriate for the individual patient.

- A service for people with Huntington's Disease that supports a network of outreach services throughout a wider region. At the time of the visit, the staff were negotiating with health authorities for funds to employ locally-based community nurses to provide initial assessment and domiciliary support.

- One neuro-behavioural unit that has developed a coaching system in its inpatient units, in which specialist staff do not only work directly with individual patients but also complete assessments, develop treatment programmes, and then train each patient's key worker, often a nurse, to deliver treatment to their patient. This has the advantage of simplifying the delivery of care for patients who experience problems in dealing with social interactions.

Residential and Respite Care

255   Most of the providers visited reported a shortage of residential and respite care homes with the skills to provide care for each of the three client groups. People with early onset dementia are usually placed in facilities that provide eldercare, although sufferers are more physically fit and disruptive than the remaining residents. There is a particular shortfall in facilities for people with Huntington's Disease, especially for those who are in the terminal phases of the disorder.

is due to be passed from one service to another. This problem can be reduced when there are defined care pathways agreed between services, which identify which agency is responsible for which categories of patients at identified stages of their disorders, and where there are protocols for referral to other services. The visiting teams found that most districts have no clear care pathways of this kind for the three client groups. This results in failure to complete comprehensive assessments, delays in referral (even where an appropriate local service was available), and confusion and distress for patients and carers.

Improving Service Articulation

266   The visiting teams identified some examples of good practice in which steps have been taken to improve service articulation.

- In a number of districts specialist neuropsychiatry and neuropsychology posts have been developed. Usually, the postholders have acted as foci and advocates for the development of better integrated and more responsive patterns of service collaboration.

- One service for people with Huntington's Disease aims to provide continuity of clinical care for all people with the disorder from initial identification to terminal care.

- One social services department was setting up a team to specialise in brain injury in order to provide care management and case finding by establishing links with the trauma and neurological rehabilitation services.

- One NHS trust has grouped neurological and specialist neuropsychiatric services for people with acquired brain injury into a Neuro-behavioural Directorate, as a means of improving liaison and continuity of care.

A Strategy for the Future

CHAPTER 7

A Summary of
Key Concepts
and Challenges

CONCEPTS

Planning and Organising Services

CHALLENGES

1   When a person develops a progressive brain disease much can be done, medically and socially, to reduce its impact on them and their family.

To challenge the view that there is little that can be done for these people so there is little reason to target resources on them. Early and effective deployment of resources while, initially, expensive will reap savings over time. This can be achieved by distributing the expenditure and effective use of ECRs.

2   Service planning should be based on knowledge of the local incidence and prevalence of the relevant disorders. These are:

- acquired brain injury in all its forms and diagnostic categories;

- Huntington's Disease;

- early onset dementia.

To accurately determine the local prevalence and incidence of these disorders, or use figures from elsewhere if this is not possible.

Not to use lack of knowledge and information as an excuse for inactivity.

To commission a survey of incidence and prevalence of each disorder with clear goals to report within a short, but realistic, period of time.

3   The planning process should include advice from professionals who are expert in this field.

To actively seek and use local expertise, and/or to seek advice from elsewhere, as necessary.

4   The planning process should address the problems raised by users and carers. These will vary from district to district depending upon the components of services that are presently available.

To find out what are the views of the local people who are affected by these disorders.

To use their views to shape priorities.

5   In most districts, the existing mental healthcare for people in these groups is very limited, with poor inter-agency collaboration and communication.

To find out from local providers what is being provided now and match this against best practice.

6   People with brain disease and brain damage are at greater risk of mental health problems and disorders than the general population, and so are their carers.

To benchmark the local picture of anticipated adequate service provision and practice against that for adequate services provided elsewhere.

To ensure that those at the greatest risk are best served by local services.

CONCEPTS

CHALLENGES

7   Neurological and psychiatric co-morbidity can lead each professional discipline to view the affected person as another discipline's responsibility. This is to be avoided. Multi-disciplinary approaches to service philosophy, design and best practice are strongly advocated.

To establish clear and unambiguous guidelines and trigger criteria as to who should be involved with which patients and when. It is particularly important to name these disorders and the spectrum of anticipated liaison arrangements in contracts with mental health providers because the needs of sufferers and their carers are multi-focal.

To establish clear expectations of co-ordinated care delivered by a variety of agencies and disciplines in planned ways within the overarching strategy and as a central principle of service design.

The positive impact of this expertise and of a single point of provider advocacy for service development should be supported by the statutory sector commissioners developing their own expertise in understanding the client groups by:

· establishing an expert advisory panel;

· actively seeking the views of users and carers;

· learning lessons from other successful centres;

· developing strong cross-sectoral partnerships;

· harnessing the experience of the non-statutory sector;

· conducting a local needs assessment.

8   There is a need to develop increased local, inter-agency, cross-district, and supra-district expertise in the diagnosis and management of these conditions.

To create imaginative patterns of collaboration with adjacent purchasers and commissioners which can make much more effective use of the often substantial monies spent recurrently on extra-contractual referrals.

CONCEPTS	CHALLENGES

Assessment

1	When a person becomes impaired in their cognition and reasoning, emotion and behaviour, the cause may be brain disease. Some such diseases are curable, some are treatable and others are progressive. Assessment is the first part of the clinical management process. In order to ensure accuracy of diagnosis (thereby establishing the cause), assessment must include a detailed interview with each patient, followed by clinical testing and investigation.	To ensure that there is a source of local expertise and experience, or a plan to develop such a resource. Experience indicates that the best way to develop this expertise is for one clinician to take responsibility for neuropsychiatric disorders in general, or for a particular diagnostic group.
2	Delays in the assessment process have a negative impact upon the health and well-being of patients and their family.	To avoid delays in referral by establishing a clear point of referral for people with suspected early onset dementia, Huntington's Disease and problems following brain injury.
3	The assessment of brain injured people involves making diagnoses (such as that of epilepsy and clinical depression) and identifying areas of impaired and intact brain function. The assessment of brain injured people should lead to goals being set for rehabilitation, with the overarching aim of increasing each person's independence and range of self-expression.	To ensure that the initial and ongoing assessments are multi-disciplinary processes that are informed by clear goal setting and clinical review. Clinical staffs should have access to the full range of diagnostic skills, procedures and resources.
4	Assessment is a continuing and interactive process conducted recurrently throughout a programme of care. In early onset dementia, early diagnosis and identification of any treatable causes will lead to less persisting disability.	To ensure that organisational factors which can be changed, but often are not, do not lead to avoidable delays in assessment, investigation, the communication of results and active intervention.
5	Severe brain damage and progressive brain disease always lead to changes in mental health (including impairment in cognition and reasoning, and emotion, behaviour and other problems).	To avoid thinking that brain disease demands only adequate neurological and rehabilitation medicine services.
6	Genetic testing can provide information on the likelihood of	To provide easy access to genetic services which should include

CONCEPTS

CHALLENGES

relatives developing several disorders but providing this information can be a major stressor in itself and any testing should be accompanied by counselling.

pre- and post-testing support and counselling.

Rehabilitation

1   Diagnosis is only the first stage in the clinical management process. Following diagnosis, any treatable, reversible condition should be treated. Symptoms that present problems in progressive conditions should also be treated actively (eg agitation, irritability, depression).

To ensure there are links between the diagnostic, rehabilitation and continuing care services, bearing in mind that these may, and often are, based in different trusts. Contracts should specify the requirement for cross-trust access for patients to professionals and facilities and likewise for their clinical attendants. Contracts should require collaboration in the care planning across trusts and enable key workers employed by one agency to carry out their duties despite the existence of organisational boundaries within the NHS and between the NHS and other sectors of care.

2   Rehabilitation services are important components of services for all people with brain injury and disease. In the case of brain injury, the intention is to accelerate recovery and to diminish the risks of permanent disabilities. In dementia, the focus is on preserving autonomy and independence and the ability to live at home for as long as possible.

The specifications for comprehensive services should be led by an analysis of needs and appropriate service options. This should include an appraisal of the role of rehabilitation for each of the client groups and prediction of the services required from knowledge gained through local needs assessments and mapping of the pattern of existing services.

Longer Term Clinical Management and Care

1   Problematic symptoms develop and change over time.

To ensure that in all of the conditions considered in this report, assessment is the first step in clinical management and not an end in itself. Assessments should not become disconnected from the goal of ensuring continuity of clinical care.

2   When a person has suffered a brain injury, the cause of the

To ensure that professionals dealing with people with these

CONCEPTS

person's problem is known but new disorders may develop subsequently and this may impair mental health but be amenable to treatment (eg epilepsy, hydrocephalus, clinical depression).

3   People with brain disorders develop the same mental illnesses as the rest of the population but with greater frequency. Most are amenable to treatment.

4   When people who are known to have serious brain disease or damage develop acute psychiatric disorder, these secondary disorders may be missed by health professionals, or may be viewed as understandable reactions or be seen as untreatable.

5   The clinical care of brain injured people can involve several NHS trusts simultaneously and serially, as well as social services departments and voluntary and private sector providers. The potential for communication breakdowns and discontinuity is considerable.

6   Brain injury injures families and social networks.

7   A high proportion of carers of people with severe brain injury, Huntington's Disease and early onset dementia experience continuing or recurrent anxiety, distress and depression.

8   The Care Programme Approach should be applied to everyone taken on by a mental health service for care. Complex care programmes are needed for people with problems that lie in these diagnostic groups. The Care

CHALLENGES

conditions have adequate training and support.

To ensure that people with these conditions are not refused or excluded from treatment because their physical disabilities make them more difficult to care for on acute psychiatric wards.

To ensure that there are professionals in each area who have sufficient special training, experience and knowledge of the three client groups to be able to avoid these risks.

To ensure that organisational features such as the purchaser-provider system, enhance service delivery and do not act against the best interests of the patients.

To ensure that a service does not only cater solely for the medical needs of people with a condition but also for the social and psychological consequences of it within a wider network of people.

To provide acceptable support for carers (including day, respite and crisis care for users) that allows them to continue in their home-based caring role for as long as possible.

To ensure that people who have one of these diagnoses are managed through a process that uses the principles that underpin the Care Programme Approach. Local case registers should be developed within explicit and

CONCEPTS

Programme Approach can help to ensure that their wide ranging needs are addressed and that gaps in provision are identified.

9   Care co-ordinators, care and case managers and link nurses can greatly improve continuity of care and reduce carer distress. This can lead to more effective use of health resources by preventing crises that may result in lengthy hospital admissions.

10 Non-statutory agencies can provide daycare and support that is viewed as less stigmatising and more acceptable to users and carers than some alternatives that are provided in the statutory sector.

11 Carers of people with early onset dementia are most distressed when an index person develops aggressive behaviour, restlessness, tearfulness or impaired sleep. All of these can lead to hospital admission for trials of treatment. Early dementia and Huntington's Disease may lead to particular difficulties in deciding the appropriate place for admission when a family is in a crisis.

12 The medical and social needs of people with severe brain disorders overlap and interact. A narrow approach to allocating responsibilities for care is an uninformed one and will usually be counter-productive.

CHALLENGES

negotiated ethical guidelines. They should contain information on the key problems and diagnoses of people who require complex programmes of care.

To consider commissioning posts for staff to conduct these duties. They can prove a valuable investment as they put people in touch with the wide range of existing services, as well as highlighting and partially resolving some of the deficiencies.

To facilitate the development of local branches of national non-statutory agencies, such as the Alzheimer's Disease Society, the Huntington's Disease Association and Headway.

To identify facilities to which people with these problems may be admitted if the need arises. It is important to consider this question before crises occur.

To develop guidelines for determining which service takes the lead in each type of case. They should include an agreed mechanism for resolving disputes speedily.

CHAPTER 8

A Strategic Approach to
Commissioning and
Providing Services

THE NEED FOR A STRATEGIC APPROACH

267 When dealing with groups of patients whose absolute number is relatively small but whose needs are very complex, there is a temptation to conclude that focusing particular attention on them is inappropriate, disproportionately expensive or unnecessary as neighbouring specialist services can be purchased, as and when necessary, on an ECR basis without deflecting attention from other priorities. The experience of the HAS in conducting the six reviews of service in this project indicate plainly that a strategic approach to commissioning and providing services for these client groups can lead to an enormous increase in the quality and appropriateness of service delivery without a proportionate associated increase in costs. It is possible for health authorities, social services departments, purchasers and providers to improve service delivery with relatively simple manoeuvres and point with pride to a service model that can be emulated elsewhere.

268 Moreover, failure to do this runs the risk of leaving groups of people who are likely to make continuing and accumulating demands on services, cared for in sub-optimal ways at best and the true expenditure on them unrealised and unplanned. Sustaining and developing low volume but highly expert services that relate well to primary care and other direct access services requires an appropriate balance of risk-sharing between:

- service commissioning and purchasing partners within each district;

- health and social services commissioners in adjacent districts, counties and boroughs;

- commissioners, purchasers, including GP fundholders and relevant providers;

- commissioners, statutory sector providers and the appropriate non-statutory sector agencies.

269 One useful approach to strategic commissioning and providing is offered by considering the natural history of each condition. As chapter four indicates, the natural history of each of the three conditions under review here is now well known. Examination of each shows that the patients' clinical conditions change in relatively predictable ways. Consequently, a patient's needs are also likely to change in the same relatively predictable ways. This means that plans can be made and that strategic commissioning is possible despite the relatively low volume of cases.

270 Without a strategy, patients may receive inappropriate, expensive and ineffective services that do not match their needs.

271 The natural histories of the three conditions have clear implications for service concepts, design, commissioning, purchasing and delivery. In the three sections that follow, the figures (Figs 5, 6 and 7) demonstrate the changing clinical conditions and changing needs for service of the three groups of patients.

272 An approach developed from awareness of these patterns over time, delivered by different professions, is likely to result in commissioning, purchasing and service delivery that is truly patient-centred. In a model of this kind, it is easy to see the role that the opinions of users and

carers may play in providing advice as to the way forward. Furthermore, this approach stresses a vehicle for understanding and therefore planning flexible service responses that these three client groups require.

273   Nevertheless, there is also a need to consider service organisation from the provider perspective (ie service structure) and as a vehicle for the delivery of strategy. So in the closing part of this chapter, the HAS presents its four tier approach to service design. This concept has been developed alongside other contemporary HAS thematic reviews in order to foster a truly comprehensive service.

274   The intention is that these two conceptual approaches - one based on knowledge of the natural history of the disorders and the second based on service design consequent on the wide-ranging needs of patients in each client group – should interlock. In other words, the HAS recommends that commissioners, purchasers and providers should use both approaches in complementary ways to test the adequacy of their services, to conceive and grasp the complexities of service agency inter-relationships required and to develop new service strategies.

275   In the next three sections, the natural history approach to service requirements and their deployment is illustrated and the structural approach concludes this chapter.

ACQUIRED BRAIN INJURY

Introduction

276   The strategic approach recommended here is illustrated by Figure 5.
The sections that follow enlarge upon the needs of people with ABI in
each of the three principal phases of their care.

Figure 5

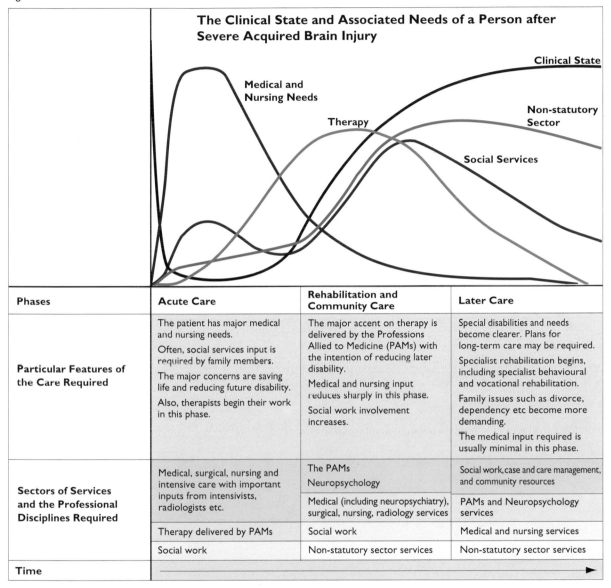

The Clinical State and Associated Needs of a Person after Severe Acquired Brain Injury

Phases	Acute Care	Rehabilitation and Community Care	Later Care
Particular Features of the Care Required	The patient has major medical and nursing needs. Often, social services input is required by family members. The major concerns are saving life and reducing future disability. Also, therapists begin their work in this phase.	The major accent on therapy is delivered by the Professions Allied to Medicine (PAMs) with the intention of reducing later disability. Medical and nursing input reduces sharply in this phase. Social work involvement increases.	Special disabilities and needs become clearer. Plans for long-term care may be required. Specialist rehabilitation begins, including specialist behavioural and vocational rehabilitation. Family issues such as divorce, dependency etc become more demanding. The medical input required is usually minimal in this phase.
Sectors of Services and the Professional Disciplines Required	Medical, surgical, nursing and intensive care with important inputs from intensivists, radiologists etc.	The PAMs Neuropsychology	Social work, case and care management, and community resources
		Medical (including neuropsychiatry), surgical, nursing, radiology services	PAMs and Neuropsychology services
	Therapy delivered by PAMs	Social work	Medical and nursing services
	Social work	Non-statutory sector services	Non-statutory sector services
Time	→		

The Acute Phase

Resuscitation, Immediate Care and Initial Medical Treatment

277   The management of patients after ABI may be considered to fall into
predictable stages. Before the acute injury, such a person is usually living
a normal life and does not need any services, although some may have
needed help with, for example, substance misuse. Then the injury
happens. The first, medical, stage of management immediately follows. A
severely injured patient is likely to need the full range of ITU services

while his or her condition is stabilised, and he or she is monitored for various complications such as brain swelling, infection, or bleeding inside the head. Initially, many patients are physically very dependant, and they need nursing and medical and/or surgical services. Usually, the treatment team is led most appropriately at this stage by a physician who is a specialist in ITU work (an intensivist).

Prevention of Disability

278   The initial focus is heavily upon medical and nursing care. Over the next days or weeks, a patient is likely to become medically more stable, and the emphasis of care changes to the reduction or (better) prevention of excess disabilities, such as contractures, chest infections and skin breakdown, and beginning physical mobilisation. The specialists who are of particular importance now are those who offer medical, nursing and physiotherapy care. Nonetheless, many other relevant specialists (eg those in occupational therapy, speech therapy, psychology, social work, vocational specialist and education) may want to begin to make their initial examinations. At this stage, the clinical team should continue to be directed by a medical doctor.

Managing Families

279   Managing patients also implies helping family members. Managing a family as well as the patient makes good clinical and economic sense. When a family is helped to cope early on, its members will be better able to help their injured relative after his or her discharge. Also, they will need less help themselves in dealing with the long-term effects of injury. This reduces the load on GPs and the social services over the coming months and years. Help for families early on is often carried out or co-ordinated by medical and nursing staff who provide information and support. Later, this help should be provided by social workers and by staff of the voluntary and charitable sector organisations, particularly Headway - the National Head Injuries Association.

The Phases of Rehabilitation and Community Care

280   As medical needs reduce, the management focus changes. It moves to rehabilitation. This should take place in a specialist inpatient brain injury rehabilitation unit. If no unit is available, the patient may continue in a surgical or similar bed and receive rehabilitation from a multi-disciplinary team comprising specialists in rehabilitation medicine, occupational therapy, speech and language therapy, physiotherapy, neuropsychology and social work. It is important that the professionals work together as a team, that it has a recognised leader who may come from any one of a range of clinical backgrounds and need not necessarily be a doctor. Some patients may be discharged home and then return for specialist rehabilitation as an outpatient.

281   Expensive and busy doctors, therapists and psychologists should look carefully at how they organise their work in rehabilitation. A clinically- and cost-effective approach is to carry out assessments, write detailed treatment plans, and then train other staff (nursing assistants, rehabilitation workers, for instance) to carry out the treatment. This ensures that the rehabilitation treatment is sufficient while leaving the specialists to design and tailor individual programmes and monitor their

delivery and impact.

282   At this stage, the focus is the reduction of deficits or disabilities to enable an injured person to return to as full a life as possible in the community. As discharge approaches, social workers should be more heavily involved. The aim is to help the injured person to have the best quality and productivity of life. The basic approach is now a pedagogic rather than a medical one in which the injured person is viewed as someone who needs help to learn new skills, rather than as a passive recipient of medical treatment.

283   Some patients (at least in the USA where such facilities are available) are offered a third level of care or transitional rehabilitation. This is aimed directly at promoting re-entry into life in the community. The concept of transitional rehabilitation recognises the common experience that the gains many patients achieve in a conventional rehabilitation unit may disappear or fail to generalise when they return to the unstructured but ordinary confusion of everyday life.

284   Some patients are lucky enough to be offered specialist vocational rehabilitation and this can have enormous benefits by increasing greatly the chances of their successful return to competitive employment. The number of these specialist vocational programmes is increasing. Often schemes are funded by charitable monies or by European Union finance.

Longer-Term Placements

285   The deficits incurred by some patients are so severe and so pervasive that their return home or to work is an unrealistic goal. These people need a safe and sheltered environment that allows the maximum degree of dignity and personal productivity. Placements of this kind rarely exist in the UK, although individual patients may achieve appropriate care of a similar type through a case management regime that is financed from the settlement resulting from litigation. But this is the exception rather than the rule.

Challenges to Effective Case Management

286   Case management is a way of maximising the likelihood of successful treatment and community re-entry. This is a process in which a patient has a guide, advocate and organiser of therapeutic resources and clinical management. The case manager ensures that each patient's needs are identified, resources are found and deployed, goals set and tracked and quality maintained. The principles of case and care management are recognised in community care legislation.

287   In reality, experience often indicates that the management of patients after ABI breaks down when they are discharged from the acute medical and surgical services.

288   Another common problem is that faced by patients who have a very prolonged period of confusion. Often, people with problems of this nature are very difficult to manage in acute surgical or orthopaedic wards. By contrast, they are easier to manage in a more appropriate environment. This is one within which they can wander safely and under observation, and in which specialist neuropsychiatric help is available.

289   Both of the practical problems cited here illustrate the importance of a planned and co-ordinated sequence of care and resources. This demands skills that might be compared with choreography in which a skilled case manager is able to bring in to play a repertoire of differing specialisms of expertise and the resources of a range of professionals each at the appropriate and optimal time, in the appropriate sequence and for the most appropriate duration.

The Way Forward

290   In some districts, it will be best to develop a centre of expertise and excellence as a focus for all the co-ordinated activity that is required in effectively managing people after acquired brain injury.

Table 8

A Summary of the Natural History and the Associated Needs of a Person after ABI			
Phase	**Description**	**Types of intervention required** (in order of priority)	**Comments**
Acute Care	The phase of resuscitation, immediate care and initial medical and nursing treatment.	1 Medical, surgical, nursing, radiological and intensive care and investigation. 2 Physiotherapy. 3 Social work.	The prime focus is on saving life and preventing or reducing complications. Physiotherapy is started, as soon as the patient is well enough, in order to reduce disabilities.
Rehabilitation	Rehabilitation is started as soon as patients are medically stable.	1 Occupational therapy, speech and language therapy, physiotherapy, neuropsychology. 2 Social work. 3 Medical, nursing.	The prime focus is on each patient's functional abilities and on reducing disabilities.
Community Care	Arrangements for community care should be initiated at the same time as rehabilitation begins.	1 Social work. 2 Community and volunteer agencies, such as Headway. 3 Neuropsychology. 4 Occupational therapy, speech and language therapy, physiotherapy. 5 Medical (eg GP).	The core aim is to set up a stable regime that offers effective, sensitively timed and responsive case management.
Longer-term Requirements Specialist Services 1 In Support of Long-term Living Arrangements	Long-term care facilities are needed by patients whose disabilities are too severe for independent living.	1 Social work. 2 Volunteer agencies, such as Headway, and housing associations.	These services provide close supervision in community settings. Their focus is on enhancing the quality and productivity of life.
2 Behavioural Rehabilitation	Behavioural rehabilitation is required by patients whose behaviour difficulties are so severe that they cannot be managed in a conventional rehabilitation unit.	1 Neuropsychology, neuropsychiatry, nursing. 2 Occupational therapy, speech and language therapy and physiotherapy.	These services focus on reducing the behaviour deficits that reduce the patient's options for rehabilitation and community placement.

291   Where these centres are in existence, the maintenance of all the expertise that the enquiries of the HAS indicate are presently very thin and poorly distributed, is a key matter. Health authorities may need to agree together to support one such facility between several of them. This demands sophistication of inter-authority relationships and purchasing mechanisms, but is vital if hard-won experience and capacity are to be developed and not lost.

292   In other circumstances, health authorities should consider combining their resources and, thereby, their strategic positions, purchasing power,

influence and monitoring responsibilities in developing a new focus of expertise. This will require not only the sophistication of relationships already defined but also mature collaborative relationships with key service providers based on overtly negotiated sharing of the risk.

293 Notwithstanding the service developments recommended in this report, the most minimum components of service that each district should satisfy itself that are in place include:

- an identified lead clinician who is experienced in managing people after ABI;

- a clear set of arrangements for effective interaction between the various services and specialisms required to mount an effective service for people after ABI, regardless of whether this involves working across one or more boundaries between trusts;

- effective protocols for interaction between the NHS and:

  - the staff of the relevant social services departments;

  - the staff of appropriate non-statutory sector agencies;

- a protocol that identifies how staff in the primary care services are able to:

  - refer their patients for specialist care;

  - gain role support and advice from a specialist provider offering the necessary expertise;

- effective arrangements for case and care management of people after ABI offered by professionals who have the necessary skills, experience and expertise;

- the capacity for case managers to call on expertise and resources from a variety of providers and agencies when these could be optimally applied.

294 Earlier in this chapter, it was established that there is a broadly predictable pattern to the care required by people after ABI. This enables a strategic approach to be taken to planning that is in accord with the clinical realities of service delivery and in a way that takes account of what the HAS has learned to be the core opinions of users and carers. Table 8 summarised this in a tabular way just as figure 5 illustrated the concepts that have been considered here in a complementary but different way.

295 In this report, the HAS recommends a similar approach to commissioning and delivering services for people with early onset dementia and for people with Huntington's Disease.

HUNTINGTON'S DISEASE

The Pre-symptomatic Phase

296 With advances in genetic testing, people at risk may know at a young age that they will, at a later but undetermined time, develop Huntington's Disease. Others with a family history may know that they are at risk but have not had a diagnostic test. Others again may have no idea that they are at risk.

297   So, in this condition there may be a very prolonged prodromal phase in which the patient-to-be knows that he or she is at risk, or will inevitably develop the condition. This period demands medical surveillance, although at a relatively low level. The main purpose of this is observation, monitoring of the person's mental state and counselling or, in some cases, psychiatric and/or psychological treatment (eg of depression or other emotional disorder).

298   The relevant medical service may be provided by a department of neuropsychiatry or by neurology or general adult psychiatry services, and the genetics service should also be involved at the diagnostic stage, and should offer counselling and genetic testing. There should be no need for outpatient follow-up but each person's GP should be fully informed of the genetic risk and test results so that he or she can correctly diagnose problems relating to the disease as they develop.

The Symptomatic Phase

299   Eventually, the condition will become clinically evident. If a patient is under medical surveillance, the diagnosis will be made promptly. If not, often there is a regrettably long period of diagnostic confusion before a definitive diagnosis is made. Once the condition is diagnosed, routine medical care can be undertaken by the GP with support from specialist neuropsychiatry services and the non-statutory sector, particularly the Huntington's Disease Association which has some excellent information packs, including one designed specifically for GPs.

The Phases of Deterioration and Terminal Care

300   As the disease progresses, the needs of sufferers change from those met by surveillance and monitoring to the requirement of active treatment of their physical state and of any emotional and behaviour problems. Family members' needs also increase. For instance, most require access to respite care for the patient. Eventually, as the disease progresses further, long-term care may well be needed. Preferably, this should be delivered in a nursing environment which specialises in managing patients with Huntington's Disease, and which has access to experienced medical input - either from a GP or from a neuropsychiatry service.

301   Again, as in the previous section relating to ABI, the HAS recommends that a strategic approach to commissioning and delivering services for people with Huntington's disease be based on an appreciation of the epidemiology, local demography, genetics and natural history of the disorder. Figure 6 illustrates the natural history and the changing requirements over time for inputs within co-ordinated treatment programmes from a range of professionals.

Figure 6

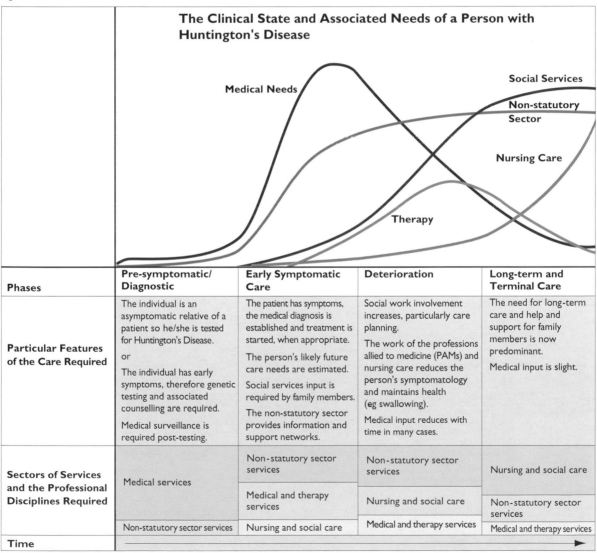

The Clinical State and Associated Needs of a Person with Huntington's Disease

Phases	Pre-symptomatic/ Diagnostic	Early Symptomatic Care	Deterioration	Long-term and Terminal Care
Particular Features of the Care Required	The individual is an asymptomatic relative of a patient so he/she is tested for Huntington's Disease. or The individual has early symptoms, therefore genetic testing and associated counselling are required. Medical surveillance is required post-testing.	The patient has symptoms, the medical diagnosis is established and treatment is started, when appropriate. The person's likely future care needs are estimated. Social services input is required by family members. The non-statutory sector provides information and support networks.	Social work involvement increases, particularly care planning. The work of the professions allied to medicine (PAMs) and nursing care reduces the person's symptomatology and maintains health (eg swallowing). Medical input reduces with time in many cases.	The need for long-term care and help and support for family members is now predominant. Medical input is slight.
Sectors of Services and the Professional Disciplines Required	Medical services	Non-statutory sector services	Non-statutory sector services	Nursing and social care
		Medical and therapy services	Nursing and social care	Non-statutory sector services
	Non-statutory sector services	Nursing and social care	Medical and therapy services	Medical and therapy services
Time	→			

302 Again, some broad phases of the progression of the disorder can be seen. While they shade from one to another, and each individual's experience will be unique, there are sufficient common experiences and a sufficiently predictable pathway to allow the entry, co-ordination, interaction and decline of the roles of service components and professionals to be planned. This pathway could be used as a tool in achieving strategic intentions through appropriate service design, resourcing, delivery and management.

303 Similarly, Table 9 illustrates this concept by summarising the tasks that face providers. Again, this indicates the complementary strategic value to commissioners, purchasers and providers of an appreciation of the natural history of Huntington's Disease.

Table 9

A Summary of the Natural History and the Associated Needs of a Person with Huntington's Disease			
Phase	**Description**	**Types of intervention required** (in order of priority)	**Comments**
Pre-symptomatic or Diagnostic Phase (prodromal)	People who are at risk are identified and diagnostic tests are offered.	1 Medical surveillance and support (genetics and neuropsychiatry). 2 Access to non-statutory sector services and support eg Huntington's Disease Association (HDA).	People at risk or those who are identified as carrying the gene, and their relatives, may need much support and counselling in this phase.
Early Symptomatic Care	Symptoms begin to appear. Patients who are under medical surveillance are readily diagnosed.	1 Medical, nursing and therapy treatment of physical symptoms and emotional and behaviour problems. 2 HDA - for information and support. 3 Social work and care management - to anticipate and plan for future care needs.	People not under medical surveillance may have months of uncertainty before a definitive diagnosis is made. In this phase, patients with HD should be managed by one specialist clinical team.
Deterioration	Symptoms worsen - particularly emotional and behavioural ones. Family members' needs for support and respite become important.	1 Medical, nursing and therapy, as above. 2 HDA, as above. 3 Social work - family support and access to respite beds.	Often, families can cope for extended periods, if they receive adequate support.
Long-term and Terminal Care	Severe dementia and physical disabilities develop.	1 Nursing and social care. 2 HDA. 3 Medical and therapy services, as above.	Now, the main focus is on the provision of long-term nursing and social care as the person deteriorates. The nursing and social care should be delivered by specialists who have experience of working with people who have HD.

EARLY ONSET DEMENTIA

Introduction

304 Chapter 4 and Table 4 indicate that, although dementia of Alzheimer type (DAT) is most common, there is a wide variety of causes of dementia in younger people. Often, the early clinical presentation of DAT is that of memory impairment together with emotional changes. In the case of dementias caused by other disorders, there may be other cognitive problems such as impairment of language, thinking, planning or the skills required to execute actions. Emotional problems are the rule, as is increasing confusion.

The Symptomatic Phase

305 The first priority is to make an accurate diagnosis so that a planned approach to care management can be adopted. Most GPs are able to recognise the early signs of dementia, although a definitive diagnosis is usually made by trying positively to exclude common causes and by trying to positively exclude other potential (and treatable) causes of each person's condition. Referral for a specialist assessment is appropriate in people who are thought to have early onset dementia.

306 Once a diagnosis has been made, it is important that medical surveillance continues. The day-to-day management of people with the early stages of dementia is now a matter for a practice nurse (to provide surveillance and advice and counselling for families), with the local authority or a non-statutory sector agency providing support through a day centre. Some day centres are also provided by the local mental health services for older people.

The Phase of Deterioration and The Long-term and Terminal Care Phase

307 As dementia progresses, there is increasing need for respite care, initially for short and then for increasingly long periods. Eventually, some demented people will need a permanent place in a nursing home that specialises in the management of confused people.

308 Once again, similar strategic concepts arise from:

- the importance of early diagnosis;

- the importance of early and forward-looking planning of care;

- the predictable course of the disease;

- the increasing dependency of most patients;

- the mixture of physical, emotional, behavioural and mental health challenges that are presented to service designers, service managers and practitioners by dementia;

- the long timespan during which individuals and their families are likely to require increasing but changing types of services.

309 These matters are illustrated graphically by Figure 7 and summarised in Table 10, overleaf.

Figure 7

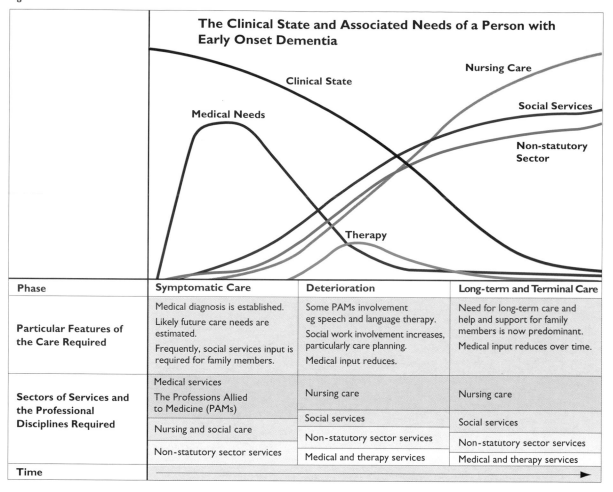

The Clinical State and Associated Needs of a Person with Early Onset Dementia

Phase	Symptomatic Care	Deterioration	Long-term and Terminal Care
Particular Features of the Care Required	Medical diagnosis is established. Likely future care needs are estimated. Frequently, social services input is required for family members.	Some PAMs involvement eg speech and language therapy. Social work involvement increases, particularly care planning. Medical input reduces.	Need for long-term care and help and support for family members is now predominant. Medical input reduces over time.
Sectors of Services and the Professional Disciplines Required	Medical services / The Professions Allied to Medicine (PAMs) / Nursing and social care / Non-statutory sector services	Nursing care / Social services / Non-statutory sector services / Medical and therapy services	Nursing care / Social services / Non-statutory sector services / Medical and therapy services
Time			

Table 10

A Summary of the Natural History and the Associated Needs of a Person with Early Onset Dementia

Phase	Description	Types of intervention required (in order of priority)	Comments
Symptomatic Care	Symptoms begin to appear and a definite diagnosis is established in this phase. The needs of patients and their families for care and support should be anticipated.	1 Medical - definitive diagnosis. 2 Social work - to anticipate care needs and help family. 3 Non-statutory sector agencies, particularly the Alzheimer's Disease Society (ADS).	The main issue is diagnosis. Future needs for care should be anticipated and plans made now. Alternative options for care should be identified and discussed with patients and families.
Deterioration	In this phase, symptoms worsen - particularly the emotional and behavioural ones. Families may have problems in coping.	1 Medical (GP) and therapy services and practice nursing. 2 ADS. 3 Social work.	Medical needs reduce in this phase. Nursing and social care needs increase - often patients require day centres and access to respite beds. Families require education and support - usually from the ADS, practice nurses and social workers.
Long-term and Terminal Care	Deterioration is more severe in this phase. The patient's personality begins to fragment.	1 Social work, including the provision of long-term care, is required. 2 ADS. 3 Nursing care, conducted with medical supervision of the patient, is prominent together with diminishing inputs from physical therapists.	Now medical needs are much less. The main requirement is for adequate long-term nursing and social care. This is most effective when provided in close inter-disciplinary collaboration. Often, this needs to be delivered in a residential setting.

SOME GENERAL CONCLUSIONS ARISING FROM STUDY OF THE NATURAL HISTORIES OF THE DISORDERS

310   This chapter has identified the strategic advantage that can be gained from a good knowledge of the natural history of each of these disorders. All three share having a predictable, but long-term natural history. Readers will be aware of other similarities that link these three disorders and, indeed, many others. Some of those that have a particular impact on the development of strategy and service management are cited here.

- Clarity of purpose and vision are essential in planning services for people who have complex problems. This requires a designated leader who has, or is willing to acquire, expertise in the subject. If necessary, advice should be sought from acknowledged experts in the field and from outside the district.

- Service planning should be based on comprehensive assessments of need. This may be based on national norms, but is much more accurate if local information is also obtained. It is important that an accurate estimation is made. Currently, most districts do not provide a satisfactory service for all three groups of people and they may not be aware of the shortfall.

- Service users and carers should be consulted in order to develop effective provision. Their opinions are important, especially when considered alongside the views of professional experts. Service users should be seen as pivotal to the strategic development of services.

- People with any of these three types of disorder have a range of health and social care needs. They require a range of types of treatment and care that cross the boundaries between providers. Partnerships between the agencies involved should be encouraged in order that efficient and comprehensive services are delivered.

- Due to the multi-faceted nature of the problems presented by people in all three groups of disorder, a co-ordinated approach to their management is required. This can be delivered by a case or care management concept wherein each person is allocated a skilled and experienced member of staff who is responsible for planning and orchestrating a comprehensive package of care.

- Often patients need to use several services at one time, or to move through different services sequentially in the course of their disease. Ease of travel may be facilitated by ensuring that the various services recognise their links and actively collaborate.

- The highly specialised nature of the work required by people with these kinds of disorder means that staff need continuing training, supervision and support.

- Wide promulgation and promotion of services will allow those in need, and other providers, to know of their existence.

- It is important to recognise that the needs of the patient do not end after the acute stage of their management has been completed. The three types of disorder considered in this report often have a lengthy course and people who suffer them have health and social care needs over long periods of time. It is important that individuals and their families are not abandoned after immediate treatment, but that they are offered continuing surveillance, intervention and care.

- The highly specialised nature of their work may mean that professionals feel isolated from general services. Contact with centres of excellence and other people doing similar work can help to reduce professional parochialism.

A STRUCTURAL APPROACH TO SERVICE DESIGN AND COMMISSIONING

A Tiered Approach to Service Structure

311 As indicated earlier, it is important to consider strategy and therefore commissioning, purchasing and service delivery from a variety of perspectives. The first approach described in this chapter has utilised the broadly predictable and phased pathways of the progression of people in each of these three groups of disorder to enable service responses to be predicted in response to assessed needs. The remaining paragraphs of this chapter summarise a complementary provider-orientated approach that endeavours to order service commissioning and delivery according to the complexity, level of specialisation and degree of inter-agency activity that each group of people requires.

312 In order to resolve a number of similar strategic challenges that arise in respect of:

- child and adolescent mental health services; and

- services for children and young people who use and misuse substances,

  the HAS has already recommended and tested a strategic approach to service commissioning, purchasing and delivery that is based on four tiers of provision. Readers are referred to chapter 8 in *Together We Stand* (HMSO, 1995) and chapter 8 in *The Substance of Young Needs* (HMSO, 1996) for further detail.

313 A similar structure is now put forward for organising services for understanding, planning, organising, delivering and co-ordinating comprehensive service responses for each of the three client groups that are considered in this report.

The Four Tiers

Tier 1

314 Tier 1 consists of those services that are in direct contact with the public (eg by primary healthcare teams, by the voluntary sector and by social services teams).

Tier 2

315 Tier 2 consists of those services that are provided by a range of local specialist services that have other primary responsibilities but which provide at least one component of the services that are required within the care plans and programmes of patients in the three client groups considered in this report (eg those services that are provided by generalists, specialists and by community mental health teams).

Tier 3

316   Tier 3 services are those very specialised services that are provided by teams of people drawn from within the district. Each team would be formed (eg by care co-ordinators, specialist neuropsychiatrists, neuropsychologists, social workers and the professions allied to medicine) with the specific role of providing and co-ordinating the provision of more specialised service elements for patients from one or more of the three client groups identified in this report. Viewed in this way, teams may be formed around the task of meeting the needs of individual patients or remain in existence over periods of time.

Tier 4

317   Tier 4 services are those very specialised services that are provided by teams of professionals from centres of expertise and excellence (eg by teams formed from specialist neuropsychiatrists, neuropsychologists and other professions who work together habitually from bases in specialist units). They may be based in specialist units that lie inside or outside any one district. The service components that the staff of a more remote but very specialised unit might contribute include:

●   admission of certain individuals for specific tasks in diagnosis, testing, multi-disciplinary assessment, reassessment and review;

●   specialist rehabilitation;

●   behavioural rehabilitation;

●   admission of certain individuals in order to provide certain targeted aspects of therapy that are identified in the treatment plan;

●   outpatient review, advice and follow-up;

●   second opinions;

●   advice delivered through consultation with staff of local services concerning their own assessment and management of individual cases;

●   role support to key specialists within districts without very specialised centres;

●   teaching and training of key local staff;

●   development of treatment approaches and techniques that are increasingly evidence-based;

●   advice to the health and local authorities on service design and delivery.

318   Each district should be able to offer Tier 1, 2 and 3 services from resources that are provided within the district, while, viewed from a national perspective, Tier 4 services will be relatively few in number, serving populations of 2-3 million but distributed geographically so that they are able to support Tier 2 and 3 services in surrounding districts, when appropriate.

Commissioning and
Purchasing Services

CHAPTER 9

Commissioning and
Purchasing Services

COMMISSIONING, PURCHASING AND CONTRACTING

319 There is a tendency to use the words commissioning, purchasing and contracting interchangeably. The guideline document, *Purchasing for Health* (NHS Management Executive, 1993), uses the term *purchasing* generically and draws a distinction between commissioning and purchasing that is now regarded as insufficient, given the evolution of these concepts and of policy since 1993.

320 In this review, commissioning is the umbrella term that emphasises strategy. The HAS takes commissioning to mean a strategically driven process by which purchasers (health authorities, general practitioner fundholders, social services departments etc) achieve the provision of services for their local population that are:

- tuned to their needs;

- sensitive to their opinions and advice;

- based upon an appreciation of the clinical realities; and

- evidence-based.

321 Purchasing is used to refer to the various procedures carried out ideally by purchasers and providers through negotiation to secure and monitor the services from providers.

322 Contracting, a sub-division of purchasing, is the technical set of processes by which services are purchased and the nature and level of services to be provided are formally agreed. In effect, commissioning encompasses purchasing and contracting but also implies a greater range of tasks because it is led by strategy and involves attempts to monitor, define and manage the market, thus creating a circular process.

323 Since implementation of the NHS and Community Care Act 1990, there has been a dynamic force in the system responsible for moving the purchasing of healthcare as close to patients as possible. This has led to health authorities and general practitioner fundholders experiencing shifts in the scope of their role as both commissioners and purchasers. EL(94)79, *Towards a Primary Care-Led NHS*, sets out an agenda that sees the new health authorities, that were formed on 1 April 1996 by amalgamations of the old health authorities and family health services authorities (FHSAs), taking the responsibility for commissioning at a strategic level, informed by the public and their providers (including general practitioners), while increasing the direct responsibility of GP fundholders as purchasers. The change process attributable to this initiative means that, in the future, health authorities will act primarily as the commissioners, while retaining some direct purchasing responsibilities (increasingly for more specialised services), and GP fundholders will act as major direct purchasers while retaining the role of informing commissioning decisions. In order to accommodate this change process, this thematic review uses the terms commissioning and purchasing to describe functions rather than to prescribe them to any one agency.

324 Also, it is important to recognise the differences of approach that are being taken generally by local and health authorities. The former, with conspicuous responsibilities for care management, are required to purchase packages of care for individuals, while health authorities buy sectors of care for populations. One result of this difference is that the

assessment of individuals is, in a substantial part, a purchasing role in the case of local authorities, while it lies almost entirely within the provider province in the NHS.

325   Health authorities are being urged to move away from the extra-contractual referral (ECR) of individuals or small numbers of cases. This involves a variety of techniques, including consortium and lead purchasing or the delegation of established extra-contractual referral budgets to providers, with the intention of redistributing the financial risks. Despite these differences in approach, which must be surmounted through jointly agreed strategies and priorities, and through the co-ordination of care for individuals, local authorities and health purchasers are being encouraged towards joint commissioning.

326   This chapter elaborates an idealised cycle of events for commissioners and then interprets these in relationship to the particular requirements of people who have acquired brain injury, early onset dementia or Huntington's Disease.

THE KEY PRINCIPLES OF EFFECTIVE COMMISSIONING

327   The work of the HAS on commissioning mental health services suggests an idealised approach. This has been applied to a range of services for different client groups by the HAS in its series of thematic reviews. Consequent testing of this idealised model has led to refinements and these are reflected in Figures 8 and 9.

328   The model begins with the formulation of outline strategic statements that indicate:

- the client group and its size;

- the broad nature of the problems faced by the client group;

- the general intention and scope of the services to be provided;

- the anticipated outcomes of intervention;

- the negative consequences that are to be avoided by securing the services under consideration;

- interventions were not made.

329   This triggers subsequent activity, including conducting a needs assessment and the choice of priorities. Information from those processes, when considered against knowledge of the capacities, capabilities, distribution and problems of present services, then empowers commissioners to plan, negotiate and agree the agenda for change, to develop more detailed service specifications, and determine the targets for monitoring and evaluation. All of these steps are vital in seeing change and developments implemented in local services.

Figure 8

An Idealised Approach to Commissioning Mental Health Services

330   As Figure 8 indicates, this is a dynamic, circular process. Inevitably, it is an iterative process that takes more than one year to complete satisfactorily. Thus, year-on-year, this strategic approach should build up and lead to the refinement of comprehensive commissioning plans. Given good interaction with service providers, this approach should also see more focused and targeted approaches to improving the delivery and quality of patient care services.

331   It is important that everyone concerned operates to agreed criteria, that the outline strategy and the role of partner agencies in achieving it is negotiated and agreed and that the definitions used for recording data and providing services are complementary.

332   Ideally, the route from an outline to a more detailed strategy passes through a number of stages. Determining priorities is key and one of the most demanding steps in the process. Health needs assessment should lead to consideration of the clinical realities, health gain issues, the evidence-base for intervention and user and carer opinions in coming to a balanced perspective on realistic goals for local services. This should enable the goals to be set for local services that reflect awareness of the capabilities and capacities of existing services, which have been clarified by mapping local resources. This background information, and the interactional collaborative processes that are implied in collecting it, should make the priorities for current service purchasing and future developments easier to agree and should result in a realistic and challenging strategy. These processes are summarised by Figure 9. Indeed, the work of the HAS, in following through implementation of its earlier advice, emphasises the crucial importance of collaboration and of developing interactional processes that involve all the key local staff in working together. Equally, the work of the HAS has also shown the relative sterility of this work when local staff are not fully engaged in conducting it.

Figure 9

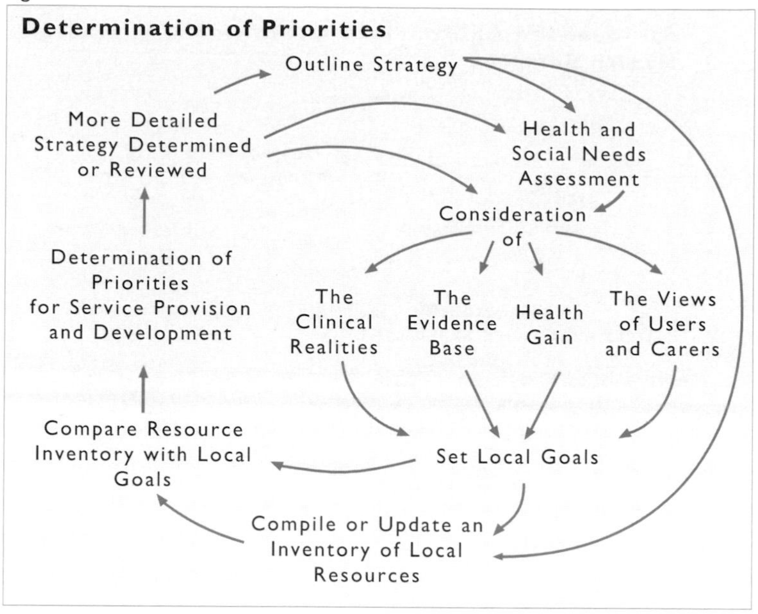

Determination of Priorities

Outline Strategy

More Detailed Strategy Determined or Reviewed

Health and Social Needs Assessment

Consideration of

Determination of Priorities for Service Provision and Development

The Clinical Realities

The Evidence Base

Health Gain

The Views of Users and Carers

Compare Resource Inventory with Local Goals

Set Local Goals

Compile or Update an Inventory of Local Resources

333   A useful guide to the process of effective commissioning is set out in *Purchasing for Health* (NHSME 1992). In relation to commissioning services, the fieldwork conducted by the HAS indicates that the following principles apply with particular force.

- It is essential that those agencies that are responsible for commissioning and purchasing services should base their approaches on a jointly agreed strategy.

- In order to enable the development of an effective commissioning approach, commissioners and purchasers must have sound knowledge of the requirements of each client group and of what is known about the effectiveness of potential interventions.

- Commissioners must be responsive to the needs of their local population if an effective climate for the strategic development of services is to be achieved.

- The development of services will be improved by mature relationships between commissioners, purchasers and service providers.

- Commissioners should collaborate with other commissioners and with purchasing organisations to form healthy alliances. This will promote consistent policy, aimed at providing integrated prevention and treatment services.

- In order to develop an effective commissioning approach to services for the client groups considered by this review, the commissioning authorities must have the appropriate organisational capability. This may require them to develop an organisational development programme for their own staff.

- In order to achieve the defined strategic goals, purchasing agencies (increasingly GPs, fundholders, SSDs and schools) must hold effective contracts with providers. These should specify proper monitoring procedures. They are best used less as enforcers and more in confirmation of negotiated agreements between purchasers and providers.

334   The Department of Health's *Practical Guidance on Joint Commissioning for Project Leaders 1995,* and the shorter, accompanying *Introduction to Joint Commissioning 1995,* provide the strongest possible encouragement to this approach, describing it as *"both an overarching strategic activity and at the same time a problem-solving tool"*. It is an approach which also integrates the strategic processes of development and needs assessment, thereby providing a holistic picture of need that is unfettered by organisational boundaries. This will provide a more substantial basis for discussions between statutory and non-statutory agencies about the services to be purchased and the co-ordination of efforts in developing networks of care.

THE SEVEN STEPPING STONES

Introduction

335   *Purchasing for Health* identifies seven stepping stones. The work of commissioning and purchasing services for the three client groups under consideration in this report is now interpreted against each of these stepping stones in turn.

Strategy

336   It is essential that authorities that are responsible for commissioning services for these client groups base their approach on a jointly agreed strategic framework. They should:

- build, wherever possible, on the existing advisory machinery and on previous strategy;

- align their strategic framework with their broader strategies for mental health services, the acute specialisms and social care provision;

- align their strategic framework and purchasing intentions with the strategies, opinions and purchasing intentions of GP fundholders;

- ensure that the strategic framework is agreed and owned by all potential agencies that have commissioning and purchasing responsibilities, thereby recognising their interdependence in producing an effective system of care;

- include a balance of assessment, treatment and support services for sufferers and carers;

- ensure that their chosen strategic approach is compatible with harnessing what is understood about the best approaches to the concepts of:

  - care pathways;

  - care planning;

  - care management;

  - case management;

  relating to each client group.

Developing the Knowledge-base

337   Commissioners and purchasers must have sound knowledge of the requirements of people who have acquired brain injury, Huntington's

Disease and early onset dementia, the different approaches to delivering high quality care and the effectiveness of potential interventions.

338 The information required to develop such a sound knowledge-base falls into a number of different categories. These include:

- the relative size and nature of the needs of the population;

- the effectiveness and targeting of services that are available;

- models of effective interagency working (including collaboration and communication between directorates, trusts and the range of health providers).

339 A sound knowledge-base may be gained through:

- understanding the nature and natural history of, and extant local care pathways for, people in each of the three groups of disorder and the services that each currently receives by:

  - agreeing with key partners (including other purchasers and providers) the definitions of illness and disability;

  - knowing about the nature and the incidence and prevalence of each disorder;

  - audit of targeted and dedicated service provision for these client groups;

  - enquiring about the relative effectiveness and acceptability of local services;

  - conducting a local survey of a wide range of professionals who are, or might be, caring for people in these groups of disorders (because existing services are often not targeted, eg young dementia sufferers are often cared for in daycare facilities intended for older people, and people with brain injury that is acquired in adulthood may be accommodated in facilities for people with a learning disability);

  - enquiring into carers' views by consulting individuals and by contacting organisations in the non-statutory sector;

  - developing awareness of the clinical and social effectiveness of particular services and of the impact of a variety of methods of education, prevention and intervention, that have been conducted locally as well as nationally;

  - developing understanding of the impact of the NHS and Community Care Act 1990, particularly with respect to the access that patients and their carers have to specialist help and individualised packages of care;

  - interrogating the databases collected within the Care Programme Approach;

  - avoidance of rigid allocation of responsibilities between social and healthcare commissioners and purchasers (though their relative roles and commitments should be clearly negotiated).

Responsiveness to the Local Population

340 Commissioners and purchasers should be responsive to the needs of their local population in achieving an effective climate for developing

their strategies and services. They should be aware of the following matters and respond appropriately.

- There may be a difference of views between users and carers in this field. Each voice should be recognised in developing and monitoring a range of services.

- Carers form a distinct constituency which requires services that are designed to meet its needs.

- Attending to carers' needs may yield additional, though often hidden, health gain by preventing deterioration in their physical and mental health and reducing the inappropriate dependency of users on formal services.

Partnerships with Providers

341 Service developments for people with problems arising from brain injury and degenerative disease are best achieved through mature relationships between commissioners, purchasers and service providers. Each agency should formulate its own service design which maps onto local areas of related expertise and provision and enables progress to be mediated through effective partnerships. Thus, these designs should be the subject of inter-agency discussion with a view to developing an agreed single design that is owned by all the relevant agencies.

342 The issues that follow are particularly significant in this field and each calls for the development of effective inter-agency partnerships.

- There is a wide variety of different providers in this field which may result in individual services having infrequent contacts with a small number of clients whose problems are at varying levels of severity. Equally, there are many individual GP fundholders who are likely to have infrequent or no contacts with people from any of these three client groups.

- There are three kinds of fundholding. General practitioners may be total fundholders; standard fundholders with year-on-year budgets, in line with the original concept; or the more minimal community fundholders, where groups of practices combine to form consortia. All of them have powers in buying elements of the services that are required by each of the client groups considered here. However, only a large consortium could consider purchasing the services against a strategy that is required by aggregated populations of hundreds of thousands of people.

- A number of providers may be in the non-statutory sector. The organisational culture of these agencies may be different to those in the statutory sector. Purchasers should endeavour to understand these differences in order to maximise their contribution to the care of these groups of people and bear in mind that voluntary sector agencies will not be able to provide a total care solution for these client groups.

- Commissioners should lead by creating a climate in which all providers operate together in the interests of clients.

- Appropriate sharing of information is enabled by mature

organisational relationships. In this setting, providers should not be burdened by requests for information for which they cannot see the relevance.

Healthy Alliances

343   Commissioning authorities should work together with other commissioners and organisations. Specialist services (Tiers 3 and 4) for people with acquired brain injury and other neuropsychiatric disorders are particularly amenable to consortia arrangements which effectively re-direct substantial collective ECR monies.

Effectiveness Through Contracting

344   Commissioning agencies and service purchasers should agree effective contracts with providers which include monitoring procedures. This means that:

- contracts with non-statutory providers should be based within a robust contracting framework to maximise the contribution of providers (that is, they should be longer-term, three- to five-year agreements which contain negotiated and realistic performance monitoring procedures);

- contracts should be based wherever possible on mainstream funding, thus recognising the need to convert short-term and pump-priming finance into robust financial arrangements;

- contract currencies should be appropriate and recognise:

    - the direct service needs of individuals;

    - the needs of primary care staff for role support and consultancy;

    - the needs of staff in specialised services for consultancy and role support from very specialised expert providers;

    - the importance of training, research and prevention;

- where necessary, commissioners should collaborate to purchase the highly specialised components of comprehensive services for each of the three client groups.

Organisational Fitness

345   In order to develop an effective commissioning approach for services, the commissioning authorities must have the appropriate organisational capability.

346   In this respect, commissioners may find it helpful to ask themselves a number of questions:

- who is the person who has knowledge and expertise in this field?

- how great is the organisational divide between the statutory and the non-statutory sectors?

- how senior are the people who have commissioning and purchasing responsibilities for services in this field and what ownership do the authorities themselves and their chief officers have?

- is the authority showing, or responding to, leadership in addressing the issues?

- can the authority identify the resource, if any, it is investing currently in services for these client groups? (Some commissioners have developed impressive specialist services through better use of existing resources for these patients.)

- does the organisation have a manager with designated responsibility for monitoring the effectiveness of ECRs?

- does the authority have an individual on its staff who has been tasked with leading on commissioning services for each client group and who is being supported in developing the necessary knowledge-base and organisational capacity for the authority?

- are the services provided for each client group subsumed or lost in the organisational structure, for example, are they caught between the mental health services and the acute services? (This is particularly important in relation to the disorders under consideration here. In almost all districts, two, three or more trusts may be sequentially or simultaneously involved in delivering care.)

Gaps in knowledge revealed may suggest that the commissioning agency should bring forward an organisational development plan to ensure that the necessary knowledge and expertise are put in place.

CONTRACTING WITH NON-STATUTORY SECTOR PROVIDERS

347   This is an important issue as many of the current range of services are found by the non-statutory agencies. Many are funded from charitable sources.

348   The HAS, in its earlier thematic review *Suicide Prevention - The Challenge Confronted* (1994 and reprinted in 1995 and 1996) paid particular attention to the role of non-statutory provider agencies. The HAS acknowledged that "*contractual relationships with these organisations are often ill-defined and open to the vagaries of the local financial situation.*" It continues by saying "*Commissioners should, however, recognise the effectiveness (and cost-effectiveness) of these services and should reflect this in their approach to contracting with them by seeking to secure more permanent and focused relationships with the non-statutory sector.*"

349   Comments of this nature were reiterated in the HAS report *A Place in Mind* (1995) on commissioning and providing mental health services for people who are homeless. They are seen as applying equally to the operation of agencies providing services for people who have acquired brain injury, Huntington's Disease or early onset dementia.

350   The main reasons for statutory sector commissioners entering into contractual partnerships with non-statutory organisations include:

- taking the opportunity to broaden the range of services that are available;

- offering greater cultural diversity of service provision;

- improving the access to services that is afforded to hard-to-reach groups;

- creating a plural market within which a number of providers can contribute specific elements or components of treatment and/or care, but in a well co-ordinated way;

- developing and testing effective and cost-effective interventions;

- providing the scope for evaluating the effectiveness of services that allow comparisons across a range of provider agencies.

OUT-OF-DISTRICT CONTRACTS

351 Problems are also posed for most health authorities and many GP fundholders by the need to commission and contract with services that are provided out of the district. These services tend to deal with a small number of cases and to be of high cost, due to their degree of specialisation and the relatively low volume of referrals. Generally, referrals and inpatient and daycare places are purchased on the basis of extra-contractual referrals. This renders certain very specialised services subject to disputes between agencies over who pays and how they should be paid for.

352 Additionally, lack of long-term commitments in principle and/or by contract to the longer-term use of very specialised services puts them into an unpredictable position and thereby makes their maintenance vulnerable. There is a high risk that loss of a specialised service could well be accompanied by loss of skills through dissemination of key staff and failure to achieve or maintain a critical mass of expertise and experience. These out-of-district, high-cost but low-volume services require the same rigorous commissioning and purchasing procedures, including their monitoring and evaluation, as other more local high-volume services.

CHAPTER 10

*A Commissioning
Action Plan*

ACTION STEPS

353 Commissioners should give a higher priority to meeting the needs of people with acquired brain injury, early onset dementia and Huntington's Disease because:

- people with these disorders constitute small and clearly-defined groups with severe physical, cognitive, emotional and psychiatric impairments, which have a profound impact on all areas of life and require a major input of health and social care, usually for the rest of a person's life;

- many people with these disorders do not receive at present a high quality of health or social services. Often, they are placed in inappropriate types of care such as acute hospital wards (both medical and psychiatric) and nursing homes for elderly mentally ill people, or in private hospitals distant from their friends and family;

- major improvements in services can be achieved in many districts by re-directing resources from high-cost but inappropriate placements, rather than by, necessarily, allocating additional revenue.

354 This chapter sets out a set of steps or building blocks by which commissioners and purchasers might begin to address the challenge and assess and review their progress. It is recognised that, in many cases, the relationship between these activities is not linear and that purchasers will often need to respond dynamically and opportunistically as the context within which mental health and the allied specialist services are purchased changes. Such changes may, for example, occur in the commissioning positions of partner agencies.

355 The eight action steps listed below in Table 11 are those that health and local authorities and other purchasers might employ in moving towards more effective commissioning of services for people with acquired brain injury, Huntington's Disease and early onset dementia. The timescale by which they could be achieved will depend on the starting position in each district. It is strongly recommended that each step is taken jointly by all agencies with a commissioning, purchasing or funding role. The chapter ends with a reprise of some key considerations for commissioners and purchasers in moving service provision forward.

Table 11

Action Steps
1 Agree a multi-agency approach to services for people with: - acquired brain injury - Huntington's Disease - early onset dementia
2 Determine shared priorities
3 Map and audit current services
4 Develop an outline strategy
5 Assess need
6 Consider service options and plan an agenda for change
7 Negotiate service specifications and contracts
8 Monitor the results, including outcomes

1   Agree a Multi-Agency Approach to Commissioning, Purchasing and Providing Services

Activity

356   An exercise designed to ensure that all the key agencies with a role in the commissioning of services for the three client groups are linked to facilitate effective joint working.

Key Questions

- Do we have a dialogue with all funding or commissioning agencies?

- Is this dialogue occurring at the right level of seniority in each organisation?

- Are the chief officers aware of, and supportive of, this dialogue?

- Are we utilising any joint resource for the benefit of the patients/clients/users?

- Is there a forum which includes all partner agencies in addition to any bilateral meetings?

- Has agreement been reached on who might lead/co-ordinate joint activity on service review and development?

- Do the current relationships provide a strong enough base to facilitate joint approaches to service planning, contracting, audit and evaluation?

2   Determine Shared Priorities

Activity

357   The aim of this stage is to ensure that all key agencies (both commissioners and providers) share a common set of objectives for services for people with acquired brain injury, Huntington's Disease and early onset dementia.

Key Questions

- Is there currently a dialogue between commissioning agencies about the needs of these groups of service users?

- Does the dialogue include GPs and GP fundholders?

- Is there a forum for dialogue between commissioners and the main providers (both statutory and non-statutory) of services for people with acquired brain injury, Huntington's Disease and early onset dementia?

- Is there a process for gaining the views of family carers of people with acquired brain injury, Huntington's Disease and early onset dementia, either by meeting with users and carers and surveys, or through consultation with the main representative bodies (Headway, the ADS and the HDA)?

- Have all partners given priority to improving the services received by people with acquired brain injury, Huntington's Disease and early onset dementia?

- Have they agreed a timetable for the completion of the strategic process?

- Do commissioners have access to expert advice on:

  - the needs of people with acquired brain injury, Huntington's Disease, and early onset dementia;

  - the most effective forms of treatment and care; and

  - the preferred pattern of services?

3   Map and Audit Current Services

Activity

358   An exercise designed to create an inventory of the nature and extent of all current provision within the district and of the use of services outside the district, whether purchased by formal contracts or by ECRs. This should include statutory and non-statutory providers and the provision purchased or funded by partner agencies.

Key Questions

- What do we currently purchase?

- How much does it cost?

- What is purchased by others?

- Are there gaps and overlaps?

- Are these services financially and professionally secure?

- Do we have useful information from these services?

- How does the provision in total compare to our assessment of need and identified goals?

4   Develop an Outline Strategy

Activity

359   The aim of this stage is for commissioners to agree the general intentions and pattern of services needed locally for people with acquired brain injury, Huntington's Disease and early onset dementia.

Key Questions

- Is there agreement on the total pattern of health and social services (whether provided locally or elsewhere) to which people with acquired brain injury, Huntington's Disease and early onset dementia should have access?

- Is there an agreed definition of the services that should be available to detect Huntington's Disease and to provide counselling to:

  - people at risk;

  - people positively identified as likely to develop the disease in later life; and

  - family carers?

- Has the most appropriate pattern of services been defined to ensure people with acquired brain injuries are given comprehensive psychological and psychiatric assessments, and that there are defined care pathways for their referral to specialist neuro-behavioural services after the completion of surgery and post-trauma rehabilitation?

- Is there agreement on the type of services that should be responsible for the initial diagnosis and treatment of people with early onset dementia? Should there be specialist early dementia services, or should they be provided by psychiatrists of old age and the teams that work with them?

- Is there agreement on the pattern of community and inpatient services needed for the behavioural management of people with acquired brain injury, Huntington's Disease and early onset dementia? Should these services be developed locally (either by a single commissioner or a consortium), or should they be purchased on a case-by-case basis from existing specialist services?

- Have the occupational needs of people with acquired brain injury been addressed? Are there proposals for ensuring access to sheltered employment schemes?

- Is there agreement on the pattern of continuing and terminal care (residential homes, nursing homes or hospital facilities) required for people with acquired brain injury, Huntington's Disease and early onset dementia?

- Has the pattern of respite care and other support for family carers been agreed?

5   Assess Need

Activity

360   A pragmatic exercise designed to estimate the level of provision required to satisfy the needs of the population.

Key Questions

- Do we have a common language between agencies which facilitates the identification of need?

- How are different conditions/behaviours prioritised by the range of agencies?

- Can we identify problems on a scale that is relevant for commissioning purposes?

- What is our position on out-of-district services? Is this shared?

- Have patients/clients/users and carers been fully involved in the assessment of need?

- Is there information about numbers of people in the district with these disorders, or if not, are there estimates of local incidence and prevalence based on epidemiological research?

- Has information been collected about the full range of locally-available services for people with acquired brain injury, Huntington's Disease and early onset dementia, and their families? Is there comparable information about the neurological and neurosurgical services that are responsible for early diagnosis and treatment of many people with these disorders?

- Have commissioners and purchasers identified their current expenditure on health and social care for people with acquired brain injury, Huntington's Disease and early onset dementia, taking into account health authority ECRs, social services department spot purchases and expenditure on people with these disorders who are inappropriately placed in residential, nursing home or hospital provision?

6   Consider Service Options and Plan an Agenda for Change

Activity

361   At this stage, commissioners and purchasers should review their options for ensuring that people with acquired brain injury, Huntington's Disease and early onset dementia have access to an appropriate range of health and social services. The aim is to compare what is considered desirable (on the basis of assessed need, the clinical realities, the evidence-base, experience and the opinions of users and carers) with the map of current service provision and then plan a process for implementing change after negotiated agreements with the providers of services.

Key Questions

- Is there agreement on how new services should be developed locally, and whether these should be tendered for or developed incrementally by building teams of staff with specialist skills in meeting the needs of people with acquired brain injury, Huntington's Disease and early onset dementia?

- Is there agreement on the allocation of responsibility between health and social services for commissioning continuing care and other support services in the community?

7   Negotiate Service Specifications and Contracts

Activity

362   At this stage, commissioners and purchasers should aim to confirm and then implement plans by means of service specifications and mature contracts.

Key Questions

- Is there a comprehensive set of contracts for the health and social services for people with acquired brain injury, Huntington's Disease and early onset dementia, which designate responsibility for clinical care, and which facilitate seamless clinical pathways between the different components across the several stages of treatment and care?

- Do contracts with the independent sector provide it with financial stability and maximise its contribution?

- Are commissioners using all sources of funds (MISG, STG, Joint Finance and European Union funds) to maximise available resources for these groups of service users?

8   Monitor the Results, including Outcomes

Activity

363   The final stage of work for commissioners is to develop an iterative process for monitoring the quality and outcomes of services for people with acquired brain injury, Huntington's Disease and early onset

dementia, for reviewing services, for implementing change and for further refining the emerging strategic approach.

Key Questions

- Is there a process by which commissioners can periodically review progress towards meeting the strategy, and amend the plan of action to take account of changes in demand and resources?

- Are there procedures for systematically monitoring the extent to which existing services for people with acquired brain injury, Huntington's Disease and early onset dementia provide good coverage of people in need, provide a high quality of assessment, treatment and care, and generate high levels of satisfaction among service users and carers?

- Is there a procedure that enables the impact of service development and change to be monitored and for it to feed into further reviews and maturation of the overarching strategy?

A SUMMARY OF KEY ISSUES FOR THE COMMISSIONERS AND PURCHASERS OF SERVICES

General Considerations

364   Commissioners should:

- monitor trends in the incidence of the range of disorders;

- agree and implement a district-wide strategy, that:

    - is agreed with the purchasers of services;

    - offers a clear continuum of help and support from the commissioners of other sectors of care and the appropriate purchasers of services;

- devise and implement a strategy specifically orientated to the needs of clients and carers;

- transcend organisational and funding boundaries.

Key Considerations

Purchasing Services for People with ABI

365   Some key considerations for commissioners and purchasers of services for people after ABI include:

- know the nature, natural history, impacts and consequences (family, work and leisure) of disability in people who are brain injured;

- know where patients with ABI are likely to be, and how many of them there are within the district;

- be aware that, because of their other injuries, patients with TBI may be dealt with in orthopaedic or general surgical wards where their brain injuries and their longer-term consequences may be missed, or given insufficient attention;

- have a clear statement of what they want from each service provider. Be clear about this and avoid perverse incentives that stem from double messages. For instance, if quality targets are multiple (eg effective medical treatment such that skin ulcers are avoided; maximum functional improvement in daily living skills; reduction in number of hours of care; or speedy return to work), there is the possibility of some of these pulling the therapeutic processes in the same or, at times, conflicting directions;

- integrate the roles and work of the statutory (health, social, housing and education services) and non-statutory services (Headway and others).

Commissioning and Purchasing Services for People with Huntington's Disease

366   A short summary of key issues includes:

- know the nature, natural history, impacts and consequences (family, work and leisure) of disability in people who have Huntington's Disease;

- know where patients with Huntington's Disease are likely to be, and how many of them there are within the district;

- integrate genetic counselling and neuropsychiatric services;

- anticipate long-term care needs and plan service responses from the time when the diagnosis is made;

- integrate the roles and work of the statutory and non-statutory services.

Commissioning and Purchasing Services for People with Early Onset Dementia

367   A short summary of key issues includes:

- know the nature, natural history, impacts and consequences of early onset dementia;

- know where patients with early onset dementia are likely to be, and how many of them there are within the district;

- integrate the roles and work of the statutory and non-statutory services;

- ensure that effective multi-disciplinary assessment facilities are available and clearly identified;

- ensure that the assessment services communicate clearly with the services that provide continuing care;

- be clear about who is providing mental health services for this client group and for their carers;

- anticipate future care and nursing needs and plan service responses to meet them once the diagnosis is established.

PART D

Key Issues Affecting
the Design and
Delivery of Services

CHAPTER 11

INTRODUCTION

368   An important ingredient in successfully commissioning, purchasing and providing the services that are the subject of this report is an adequate awareness of relevant legal issues. The care and treatment of the clients of these services raise a number of important legal issues ranging from the possible application of the Mental Health Act 1983 to the provision of contraception. It is neither possible nor desirable to attempt a definitive description of the relevant legal framework. What is required from those responsible for services is:

- sensitivity to the situations and circumstances where an awareness of the law is important;

- willingness to anticipate and plan in advance; and

- access to competent legal advice.

369   Some of the most difficult legal issues are concerned with lack of legal capacity and the use of restraint, and this chapter will focus upon them. It is a fundamental principle of law that the care and treatment of capable adults can only take place if they have given their valid consent, unless the law specifically provides authority for treatment and care to be conducted in the absence of valid consent. Indeed, consent to treatment is one of the key legal issues that may arise for the clients referred to in this report and those who care for them.

CONSENT TO TREATMENT

370   In law, it is presumed that everyone has mental capacity. Following brain injury or the onset of dementia, many clients may well, at law, be judged incapable of giving valid consent. The principles underlying non-consensual treatment, as derived from a number of cases, have recently been summarised as:

- in general it is a criminal and tortuous assault to perform physical invasive medical treatment without the patient's consent;

- a mentally competent patient has an absolute right to refuse to consent to medical treatment for any reason, rational or irrational, or for no reason at all, even where that decision will lead to his or her own death;

- no one can consent on behalf of a mentally incapacitated adult;

- where it is impossible for the patient to communicate a decision through unconsciousness or lack of mental competence and the treatment is not contrary to the known previously expressed decision of the (when competent) patient, it is lawful to provide treatment which is:

  - necessary to save the life, or prevent a deterioration in the physical or mental health of the patient; and

  - in the patient's best interest;

- a patient lacks the relevant mental competence to make treatment decisions if he or she is incapable of:

  - comprehending and retaining information about the proposed treatment;

- believing such information; and

- weighing such information in the balance to make a choice.

371 In essence, where an individual is assessed by the doctor proposing to treat him or her as incapable of giving valid consent then, under the common law, in many cases, that doctor would be entitled to administer that treatment provided, among other things, it is in the patient's best interest. In the main, relevant case law has only addressed situations where immediate or short-term treatments, such as some kinds of sterilisation, are proposed. There is a paucity of decisions about long-term treatments and the situation is complicated by the absence of any decision about whether care professionals, when administering such treatments, would be entitled to use any form of restraint. The Courts are likely to move cautiously in this area and, in particular, will usually look to the possible application of the Mental Health Act 1983. Guidance on the law in general and the assessment of incapacity can be found in *Assessment of Mental Capacity* (BMA and Law Society, 1995) and *The Mental Health Act Code of Practice* (HMSO, 1993; and Law Commission Report No 231).

DETENTION OF CLIENTS UNDER THE MENTAL HEALTH ACT 1983

The Background Conditions

372 The Mental Health Act 1983 is primarily concerned with providing the legal authority for the detention of mentally disordered patients in hospitals or mental nursing homes. Subsequent to their detention, most clients are subject to the Act's provisions related to consent to treatment which authorise, in some circumstances and subject to certain safeguards, the treatment of the individual's mental disorder in the absence of their consent.

373 The possible application of the Mental Health Act 1983 to some of the people referred to in this report is a difficult and, at times, controversial matter which raises a range of issues beyond the strictly legal.

374 Among the criteria that have to be satisfied before somebody can be admitted under the Mental Health Act 1983, is the requirement that they must fall within one of the legal categories of mental disorder referred to in the Act. To place somebody under the powers provided by one of the sections of the Act, an Approved Social Worker (ASW) applies, under an appropriate section, and backed by support from two independent doctors. The doctors, having clinically assessed the patient, then have to conclude whether the patient's clinical diagnosis falls within one of the legal categories.

Short-term Admissions

375 For short-term admission under the Mental Health Act 1983 (for example, admission for assessment under Section 2), "mental disorder" is defined in the Act as "*mental illness, arrested or incomplete development of mind, psychopathic disorder or any other disorder or disability of mind*". This is a broad category which includes many of the clients referred to in this report.

Longer-term Admissions

376   More problematic are longer-term admissions under the Act (for example, admission for treatment under Section 3) where the relevant categories of mental disorder are narrower, namely mental illness, mental impairment, severe mental impairment or psychopathic disorder.

377   If it is envisaged that a service may wish to use the Mental Health Act 1983 for longer-term detention as part of a patient's care and treatment, then thinking through in advance the possible general conditions relating to application of the Mental Health Act 1983 would be a worthwhile investment.

378   Taking, as an example, those people with acquired brain injury who it is felt may benefit from longer-term detention under the Act, it would be difficult to argue that they fell within the legal category "*mental impairment*" as a key component of the definition is "...*a state of arrested or incomplete development of mind...*" which implies onset in childhood and would appear to exclude acquired brain injury in adults. A more controversial and, certainly more stigmatising, category is "*psychopathic disorder*" defined as "...*a persistent disorder... which results in abnormally aggressive or seriously irresponsible conduct...*".

379   Many would argue that, if the Mental Health Act 1983 has to be deployed in these circumstances, then the legal category "*mental illness*" is to be preferred. No definition is offered in the Act and the Courts, when asked to consider this issue, concluded that "*The words... have no particular medical... legal significance... I ask myself, what would the ordinary sensible person have said about the person's condition...*". The Butler Committee report (1975, paragraph 1.13) defines mental illness as a "*disorder which has not always existed in the patient, but has developed as a condition overlaying the sufferer's usual personality*", while a DHSS consultation document published in 1976 suggested a closed definition that focused on impairment of intellectual functioning, alteration of mood beyond a certain point, delusional beliefs, abnormal perceptions or disordered thinking. In essence, the matter is left to medical clinical judgement.

380   The application of this legal category to the clients referred to in this report is problematic but it is possible to argue, in particular, that some of the signs and symptoms of the conditions under discussion might bring the individual within the category of mental illness.

Safeguards for Patients

381   The implication for a service of providing some of its care and treatment to some of its patients under the powers and conditions provided by the Mental Health Act 1983 are, of course, far wider and include the establishment of systems and procedures which deliver the safeguards included in its provisions. Those people who commission and provide such services must include compliance with these provisions in their definition of, targets for promotion of, standards for, and monitoring of, quality.

RESTRAINT

382   One advantage of placing patients under the restrictions provided by certain of the sections in the Mental Health Act 1983 is that it provides clear legal authority to stop the detained patient leaving the hospital or

mental nursing home. There are occasions when it is necessary to use some forms of restraint for clients who are not detained under the Act. This possibility is clearly envisaged by the *Mental Health Act Code of Practice* (Chapter 18) which stresses the crucial importance of clear unit policies and individual care plans which, where necessary, address this necessity.

383   It is not always easy to disentangle treatment and control, and the legal authority to proceed in the absence of an individual's consent is frequently similar in relation to both problems. Restraint under the common law can be justified, in certain circumstances, by:

- the patient's consent;

- the doctrine of necessity; and

- the prevention of harm.

384   Further, in relation to a patient being prevented from leaving hospital, the provisions of the Mental Health Act 1983 may apply.

385   All forms of restraint are subject to the legal requirement of reasonableness; that the force used is no more than is reasonably necessary to accomplish the objective for which it is allowed and that it must be in proportion to the harm threatened. One of the key ingredients, in any definition of quality for the delivery of this aspect of care and treatment, is that it is lawful. Achieving this involves not only understanding the limits of what is authorised, but, also thinking through, in advance and in practical terms, how and when restraint will be applied, the systems required to monitor its use and, equally important, adequate training for all the staff who are involved.

386   If restraint is used repeatedly, ie to prevent a person leaving premises, then the *Mental Health Act Code of Practice* (Chapter 18, paragraph 27) notes that "*consideration must be given to assessing whether they would be more appropriately formally detained under the Act.....*".

PERSONAL AND FINANCIAL MATTERS

387   Lack of legal capacity has significant consequences for the management of a client's personal, and especially their financial, affairs.

388   The law provides a number of mechanisms for dealing with these circumstances and it is important that services are adequately aware of them and facilitate clients' access to them. The most important are considered in the sections that follow:

Appointeeship

389   The Department of Social Security (DSS) has the power to appoint a suitable person to receive a client's social security benefit and income support if the latter is "*unable to act*" (Social Security (Claims and Payments) Regulations 1987, Reg 33). The "*appointee*" is entitled to spend the money received for the personal benefit of the client. It is an easily accessible procedure, although the relative lack of formal safeguards can make it susceptible to abuse.

The Court of Protection

390   At the opposite end of the scale in terms of complexity is the Court of Protection. This was established in the rein of Edward II and its

jurisdiction arises when the Court, after considering medical evidence *"is satisfied that a person is incapable, by reason of mental disorder, of managing and administering his property and affairs"* (Mental Health Act 1983, Section 94(2)). The Court of Protection can make a number of orders, the most common being the appointment of a receiver (who will deal with the client's financial affairs under the supervision of the court) or, where the patient's property is worth less than £5,000 and it is not necessary to appoint a receiver, it can make what is known as a *"short order"*. For example, such an order might direct a bank to pay a client's rent out of his or her bank account. The Court of Protection has extensive powers (including the power to make a will on behalf of an incapable person) and its powers are most frequently used when an individual's financial affairs are extensive and complex.

Enduring Power of Attorney

391   The mechanisms referred to above come into play once an individual has become incapable of managing their financial affairs. Their use is instigated by others. The Enduring Powers of Attorney Act 1985 introduced a new type of power of attorney which, unlike an ordinary power, enables somebody to appoint his or her own agent to manage their affairs once the former becomes incapable of doing so at some time in the future. An ordinary power of attorney is automatically revoked when the person giving it becomes incapable of managing their affairs and therefore, the enduring power of attorney does enable those who currently have legal capacity, but do foresee their faculties failing in the future, to make arrangements that can continue after this occurs. The procedure incorporates safeguards and is under the general jurisdiction of the Court of Protection. It is essential that those who wish to execute an enduring power of attorney seek competent legal advice so that the advantages and disadvantages of this procedure are fully explained and considered before it is embarked upon.

CONCLUSION

392   The range of legal issues that arise for the services under consideration in this HAS review and the clients they serve is broad. It is essential that all those who commission, purchase and provide these services recognise the importance of the law, not only for the dignity of the client, but also to those who care for them as well. Additionally, a good understanding of the law and its intentions can comfort and guide practitioners who face difficult decisions as how to act in the best interests of their clients and patients.

*The Principles
of Good Practice in
Service Delivery*

INTRODUCTION

393   The provision of mental health services for people with acquired brain injury, early onset dementia and Huntington's Disease is not a new requirement. The management of severe psychiatric problems consequent upon brain disease has always been a significant part of what psychiatric services do. Before the widespread mental hospital closures of the last three decades, up to 10% of the population of these institutions who were under 65 years of age had psychiatric problems consequent upon organic brain disease. While planners of community care have attempted to cater for the needs in the community of the largest diagnostic groups previously managed and cared for within mental hospitals (particularly people with chronic schizophrenia), in most districts the mental health needs of younger people with brain disease of all origins and kinds have not been addressed directly.

The Risks - Falling Through the Net of Care

394   Experience suggests that if people with these disorders do not have severe motor and sensory impairments, neurologists and rehabilitation medicine consultants are reluctant to become involved. Also, general psychiatrists are often unwilling to take on people who may occupy beds designated for acutely ill people for long periods. Hence, unless services for people in these three groups are specifically planned and commissioned, it is the experience of the authors that very little is provided and then only *in extremis*. Stated in a different way, this means that people with the most disabling and distressing co-morbidity (ie those who have both psychiatric and neurological disorders) are likely to fall through the net of care.

395   Allocating responsibility of care for these groups is confounded by at least two factors.

- Developing a condition which involves brain disease or damage and marked alterations in mental health can take the individual through the services provided by several medical specialties and often several trusts. This is not only demanding for the individual and their family but also leads to ambiguity and sometimes to disputes in deciding who holds responsibility for continuing clinical care. This is less likely to occur if there are departments or services that bridge medical disciplines, particularly those of rehabilitation medicine and neuropsychiatry.

- People who fall into these client groups have a mixture of problems that can be characterised as long-term, combining health and social needs. All too often the provision of appropriate care and residential placements is hampered by arguments as to whether the needs of individuals are predominantly social or health related. Proper provision is not possible without interagency collaboration and, even where this exists, an affected individual or family may only have their needs met with the assistance of professional advocacy or case or care management. In this context, application of the Care Programme Approach is valuable.

396   A way to avoid some of these organisational pitfalls is to plan from the individual patient's (and carer's) viewpoint. This involves identifying a pathway of care that lasts from diagnosis to death (or full recovery in

innovative arrangements using private sector resources for treatment, training and consultation.

The Role of Primary Care

407   Primary healthcare teams (PHCTs) have an important role to play in the long-term management of these conditions but their practices can be ineffective due to the lack of familiarity of staff with conditions which they see rarely. The staff of local non-statutory and statutory mental health service providing agencies, particularly care co-ordinators, case managers and link nurses, can provide the staff of PHCTs, as well as patients and their relatives, with information, and also provide continuing education for PHCTs.

CARE PROGRAMMES AND CARE PATHWAYS

The Care Programme Approach

408   The integration of health and social care and good communication are facilitated by applying the Care Programme Approach (CPA) (Department of Health, 1996). It has four main elements:

- systematic arrangements for assessing the health and social needs of each person who is accepted by the specialist mental health services;

- the formulation of a care plan which addresses the identified health and social care needs of each individual;

- the appointment of a key worker to keep in close touch with each patient and to monitor care;

- regular review and, if need be, agreed change in the care plan for each individual.

409   The CPA can be activated at two levels - minimal or complex. A complex care programme should be initiated if there is involvement of more than one agency, particularly if it requires involvement by both the health and social services. Care plans should be in written form and discussed, negotiated and agreed with users and carers.

410   Written care programmes can provide:

- enhanced mechanisms for sharing information;

- a basis for informed debate;

- mechanisms for improved purchaser-provider communication;

- a platform for evaluation and audit;

- a means of stimulating good practice (Bailey, 1995).

Care Pathways

411   A core theme in this report, indeed the central concept underlying the strategic approach recommended by the HAS, is the predictable sequence of phases in the management of people who have acquired brain injury, early onset dementia or Huntington's disease.

412   In parallel with appreciating the clinical pathways for each of the conditions, it is possible to identify a complementary desirable care pathway. Because the types of care required and the prominence of each component of care vary with the phase of each disorder, and

because each individual's needs require care provided by a range of disciplines from a variety of agencies, it is appropriate to describe these pathways as integrated care pathways.

413   Increasingly, the thinking of local authority purchasers is towards defining managed packages of care that are orientated to the assessed needs of individuals and their families. Some child and adolescent mental health services are exploring these matters now and this style of service development is advocated as another recurrent theme in this review.

414   The integration of services for these three client groups requires each agency to be specific about the types of service, assessment, interventions, treatments and facilities that it provides so that the care of individuals and their families can be programmed in ways that draw on the resources of a variety of providing organisations. Each agency and service component should be able to provide a menu of the types of work that it is able to offer. This should enable key workers to focus their advice to individuals and their families through well informed and well co-ordinated care programmes.

415   Figure 10 illustrates the hypothetical pathway of a person who has acquired a brain injury, through a programme of care provided by a number of agencies.

Figure 10

THE INTEGRATION OF THE SECTORS OF CARE

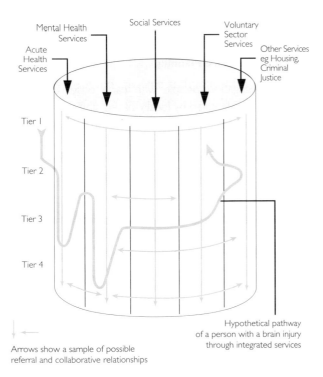

Arrows show a sample of possible referral and collaborative relationships

Hypothetical pathway of a person with a brain injury through integrated services

Support During Crises

429   If continuing support is offered to younger people with dementia by community psychiatric nurses and others, crises are likely to be avoided. Nonetheless, assessment and support are likely to be required on an urgent basis when existing care arrangements break down, and arrangements for emergency assessments must exist.

430   People with acquired brain injury, Huntington's Disease and early onset dementia sometimes experience a lack of understanding and appropriate care when they are admitted to acute hospital services, yet, in most areas, this is the only care that is available in a crisis. Therefore, the staff of acute hospitals should review their arrangements for providing appropriate care for people with these disorders.

Residential Care Facilities

431   A number of people with these disorders require continuing residential care, either because they have deteriorated and need higher levels of care or because existing family carers are unable or unwilling to continue to look after them. One possible solution is the provision of a small number of dedicated places in a wing or annex of a nursing home or residential home for older people. Alternatively, siting this facility in a residential home would be possible, but this option requires enhanced staffing levels sufficient to provide the high level of care required and this may not prove feasible.

Palliative Care

432   At present, a significant proportion of younger sufferers are living in residential care by the time they reach the terminal phase of dementia or Huntington's Disease. This situation appears to be likely to continue. However, whenever possible, sufferers should be afforded the option of dying at home. This could be achievable if hospice at home services are developed.

Support for Carers

433   A model of services for these disorders should include provision of a range of types of support for carers. Recognition of the occurrence of many instances in which children are the principal carers and of their specific needs for support must be included in a comprehensive model. Support for carers should include the provision of services for the sufferer, recognition of the importance of carers being involved in decision-making, and specific measures to support carers. The latter should include:

- provision of information (including clear information about the services that are available and routes for referral);

- benefits advice (particularly important where carers may have been forced to give up working);

- training in the techniques of providing care;

- support (particularly important for younger carers);

- bereavement counselling;

- provision of support groups.

Training and Raising Awareness

434   A major theme of the strategic approach recommended in this report is recognition of the fact that the needs of people with these disorders and their carers are different and should be met by relevant but differing responses. The success of this approach depends on specialist staff, non-specialist staff, and carers all having access to basic and continuing training that enables them to understand and deal with the special needs of younger sufferers. In addition, there is the need to improve the level of understanding of society on a wider basis. This calls for a particular focus on raising awareness of the existence and impacts of brain disorders in younger people with employers, the staff of public bodies, and the police, as they can have a great influence on the lives of sufferers and carers and on public attitudes.

CHAPTER 13

Training, Teaching and Staffing Issues

INTRODUCTION

435   Professionals who work in this field should have wide-ranging knowledge and experience of the sometimes puzzling and convoluted demands made by people with these disorders.

436   These patients require a high level of commitment from many professionals from different disciplines, and those who work in this arena quickly build up large caseloads. All of these factors combine to place great strains on services.

TRAINING

The Training Needs of the Staff of Services

General Services

437   As earlier chapters indicate, a core theme is that the mental health needs of patients require the provision of a variety of responses in an assortment of settings. These can be classified as located in general or specialist arenas. Staff in general services should have a basic knowledge of neuropsychiatric disorders.

438   Some non-specialist professionals will come across people in these client groups more than others. They require a greater level of knowledge. It should be possible to identify this group of staff within each geographical area, but their identity will depend on the particular organisation of local services. Close collaboration between professional groups and services will demonstrate deficiencies in knowledge and expertise and, thereby, identify training needs.

439   Some staff, including social workers and community psychiatric nurses, develop a particular interest in these client groups because of their initial involvement with one client, and this may provoke them to seek more information. These staff should be encouraged and offered opportunities to learn. In this way, the expertise available in the area increases and individual enterprise and motivation is fostered and rewarded.

440   The understanding of mental health issues required by staff will depend on the point in the patients' care pathways at which staff become involved. Sometimes, the staff of medical and surgical services disavow the need for awareness of mental health issues. This is a grave misunderstanding. Clearly, staff of whatever discipline cannot avoid the neuropsychiatric, psychological and social results of acquired brain injury, Huntington's Disease and early onset dementia. In many cases, they may be the ones who are best placed to identify, respond to, and deal with these matters. At the least, they should be aware of the potential for these consequences and be prepared to involve others if they cannot deal with them. In addition to knowledge of the disorder, this requires awareness of the services that exist in the area.

441   It is likely, and in many ways desirable, that the majority of patients should be dealt with by non-specialists. What is of signal importance is that intensive specialist intervention should be provided at the right time, in the most appropriate degree and in the best place in each person's pathway of care. Only the most difficult or exceptional patients will be directly or continuously managed by the specialist services. Therefore, there is a requirement for specialists to make

Costs

455 All of these different types of training should be costed and funded as it is appropriate that the outlay involved is recognised as a legitimate and expected expense. Educational matters are often forgotten and may become hidden costs. It is important that the costs inherent in providing acceptable training are explicitly recognised by purchasers as well as providers and included in the overall cost of the service.

456 The natural inclination to keep costs low is laudable, but this should not inhibit services from acquiring the best teaching available. Ultimately, both lack of training and inadequate training lead to poor clinical performance and this is to the detriment of the patients served. The price of cutting legitimate expenditure on training is paid by the clients.

The Care Programme Approach

457 Training in the use of the Care Programme Approach should take place in most districts and is relevant to staff who care for people with all mental disorders.

Case Managers

458 One of the most effective ways of supporting people with these disorders is through appointing case managers. This is a relatively new task with no agreed training path, although a professional organisation has been set up recently (the British Association of Brain Injury Case Managers) to deal with training and standards as well as other professional matters. Current case managers come from a variety of professional backgrounds. Often, the cases that they take on are highly complex and require their long-term involvement. Caseloads may vary widely. Some case managers may hold fewer than 20 active cases while others may manage very many more. Case managers are often professionally isolated and are at risk of burnout. Often their work is paid for by insurance monies.

Research and Evidence-Based Practice

459 Research on treatment approaches to the problems experienced by patients in the three client groups is particularly difficult and demands a different approach than that taken in many other clinical areas. The great variety between individual patients and the changes that occur over time make it difficult to collect clinically homogeneous groups of patients to which a single treatment approach can be rigorously applied and tested. Thus, the evidence base is often built around single cases or small groups of disparate patients with common problems. An incremental research strategy to create evidence-based clinical practice in this area should include a standardised approach to clinical assessment for people in each of these client groups. This should be followed by the centralised collection of relevant data.

Audit

460 Training matters are so important that they should not be assumed to take place. Purchasers have the right to insist on, and providers have the obligation to establish, effective means of monitoring the training offered to staff. Some specific areas of training, such as fire training, have their own special monitoring. Professional groups may have their own mechanisms, but this does not absolve the providing agency from ensuring that training is adequate.

461 Staff have an obligation to use training opportunities sensibly and efficiently. Purchasers would expect to ensure that monies expended on training are spent in an appropriate manner.

TEACHING

462 Any group of staff that has special knowledge or ability has the obligation to disseminate that knowledge. Staff should be encouraged to teach others, both within and outside a service. Members of staff need to be supported in this by their parent organisation, which should allow time and resources for dissemination of expertise.

463 It is legitimate that the teaching provided should be paid for in some way, but this generation of income should not be the single *raison d'être* for providing an educational service. Teaching is an integral part of the full role of a specialist service that deals with people who have a brain disorder and it should be integrated into the management approach, as for example, when the staff of a nursing home is taught principles of behavioural management when looking after a resident who has had brain injury. As another example, teaching of this type may include specific training for carers in how to transfer care.

464 A distinction should be made between the different kinds of teaching. That which is part of clinical management will be paid for indirectly and as a part of contracts for services, whereas a charge may be justified for training that is purely educational.

STAFFING ISSUES

The Development of Neuropsychiatry and Neuropsychology

465 During the past three decades, general psychiatric and mental health practice has gradually moved away from focusing on the management of people under 65 years with organic brain disease. The creation of the Royal College of Psychiatrists and a related membership examination in the early 1970s greatly improved specialist training in psychiatry. Nonetheless, the importance attached to skills in the allied discipline of neurology appears to have diminished in parallel with broadening of the scope and impact of other psychological and physical treatments. Recently, the Royal College of Psychiatrists has reaffirmed its view of the importance of knowledge of neurological disorders for psychiatrists and has modified its training requirements and examinations to reflect this.

466 Over the same 30-year period, knowledge of brain function in relation to behaviour has increased greatly and a small but increasing number of psychiatrists with specialised knowledge and skills in brain science and neurology have been trained to take up specialist neuropsychiatry posts.

467 The service visits conducted by the HAS for this review found that the districts with these posts had better developed services for the client groups under consideration. In addition, people with mental health problems associated with other disorders, such as Parkinson's disease and epilepsy, also benefited. Nonetheless, there is no common service specification for these posts or an established training route to them. Much the same situation pertained when other specialties, such as psychiatry of old age, were first developed. Posts in neuropsychiatry are also being created in other parts of the world, particularly the USA.

468   The position with respect to psychiatry is mirrored by similar circumstances and the development of specialisation in neurology and clinical psychology. Clinical neuropsychology began as a discipline that was concerned almost exclusively with the accurate measurement of cognitive ability. More recently, many neuropsychologists have taken on increased therapeutic and service management roles.

Community Teams

469   Most of the work done with people in these three client groups will not take place in an inpatient unit. But a comprehensive team will be necessary to conduct assessment, therapy and care in the community and to liaise with other workers. In some districts, it may be desirable to create separate special teams for some client groups, for example a service for younger people with dementia, and such a team might be found within the mental health service for older people. Again, decisions about this should be conditional on local arrangements.

470   Without a dedicated neuropsychiatry service, it is difficult to see how high quality care for these three client groups could be provided by a single team. Traditionally, they are excluded from most services because of their combined physical and psychiatric disabilities. To assume that sufferers will be dealt with by existing services, as in the past, is also to limit the adequacy of the care that is provided.

Specialist Units

471   Units must be adequately staffed if they are to run well. Experience indicates that units in which there are inadequate numbers of staff quickly turn into poor institutions, with practices designed to benefit the staff rather than the patients. In these circumstances, staff can do little more than contain their clients and ensure their basic safety. No rehabilitation work is possible and staff soon become disillusioned and lose motivation. Good staff are not attracted to units of this character and so the quality of the service provided spirals downwards.

472   On well-staffed units, there is time for rewarding work that is of benefit to the patients. Staff have time to design and implement rehabilitation programmes and to maintain their own educational standards. Work outside the unit and contact with patients before and after admission is possible. Liaison with other professionals and the staff of other agencies is facilitated and time is available to educate families and carers.

473   This approach supports the position that the complement of staff and the mix of skills and grades in any unit should be determined locally according to the philosophy, objectives and role of the specialist service or unit.

474   Planners should acquaint themselves with the staffing ratios used in other similar units and come to an informed conclusion about the right number of staff and the suitable blend of professions, grades and skills.

The Professions

Medical Staff

475   There should be a nominated medical contribution to the service for each of the three client groups. Ideally, this would be provided by a specialist in neuropsychiatry who would take the lead and work in co-ordination with specialists in neurology, neurosurgery, rehabilitation

medicine, genetics and others as appropriate. If it is not possible to create a neuropsychiatry post, or to employ a neuropsychiatrist, then the consultant should be someone with some expertise and, more importantly, with an interest in the management of these patients. A consultant who is not fully committed to the needs of these groups of patients will communicate his feelings to the rest of the team with inevitable results. The amount of consultant time involved will depend on the size of the service and its aspirations.

476   Services of this kind offer an unparalleled training opportunity for junior medical staff. Sessions of junior medical staff time should always be sought. This may be from psychiatric rotations or from trainees in rehabilitation medicine. The experience gained will increase the awareness of these issues in the next generation of doctors.

477   Currently, there is little formal training in neuropsychiatry in the UK at either senior house officer or specialty registrar level. Posts should be established in order to provide the specialists that are required in the future.

Psychologists

478   The contribution of neuropsychology should be of the highest order. A proper understanding of the cognitive and behavioural consequences of brain disorder (of whatever type) is essential to good management of patients and this is not possible unless an expert neuropsychological interpretation is available. A consultant neuropsychologist is essential in running high quality specialist services, particularly for people with ABI.

479   The role of a psychologist should not be confined to assessing intellectual functioning. Psychologists should be central to the development of rehabilitation programmes, particularly those that involve the management of behaviour.

Community Psychiatric Nurses

480   The potential roles for community psychiatric nurses cannot be overstated. Patients remarked on the practical and emotional support they receive from community psychiatric nurses. The community psychiatric nurses who are best suited to the work are those who have special experience in working with people who have chronic ill health. Therefore, they tend to be of a high grading.

481   Often, community psychiatric nurses may take on the role of case manager. The responsibilities of this task should also be reflected in the grading of the posts. Additional training should be available for nurses who take on the very demanding case management role.

482   Because of the chronic nature of the problems presented by neuropsychiatric disability, patients are often involved with services for extended periods, in some instances for life. As their caseloads increase over time, it is necessary to protect community psychiatric nurses from being overburdened.

Social Workers

483   The social issues that are faced by patients from each of the three client groups are so particular that there is a very strong argument that services for these client groups should employ specialist social workers. In this way, the social workers will gain the expertise necessary to guide

their clients. The unsatisfactory alternative is to expect a generic social worker to deal with the singular problems posed.

484   Social workers in specialist services of the nature envisaged in this report also require a thorough knowledge of the benefits system. In addition, they require a detailed knowledge of mental health legislation and how it relates to the particular client groups. For this reason, they should be approved under the Mental Health Act 1983.

Other Therapists

485   Therapists, such as physiotherapists, occupational therapists and speech and language therapists, may be employed specifically by specialist services, or may be bought from other services, such as those providing rehabilitation medicine services.

486   The amount of time needed from therapists of these disciplines will depend on the style of the specialist service and the philosophy of delivery of care. In inpatient units that use a behaviour modification approach, for example, it may be desirable for the number of staff that interacts with each patient to be controlled. In this model, other therapists may work by advising the care staff, or by performing assessments and then supervising the delivery of the therapy. In other models, the arrangements may differ in that therapists have more direct involvement with their clients. Questions of this kind should be debated and an approach agreed at the planning stage for each service and then subjected to recurrent review.

*The Implications for the
Providers of Services*

CHAPTER 14

The Clinical Task

INTRODUCTION

487 Everyone who has neurological and psychiatric co-morbidity requires:

- wide-ranging, comprehensive assessment of their needs;

- recurrent reassessments of their needs;

- appropriate and closely monitored medical management;

- support for them and their carers.

This should take place within a framework of care that encourages good communication and a willingness for different agencies to share information and responsibility for care. These aspects of best practice will be encouraged by the proper implementation of the Care Programme Approach, which can and should be applied to all patients who are cared for by specialist mental health services.

ACQUIRED BRAIN INJURY

488 The brain can be injured in a number of ways and the mode of injury has some significant influences on the pattern of resulting deficits and intact functions (see Chapter 4).

489 Whatever the cause, often the immediate result is a period of coma. During this period, the immediate care needs of the patient are plainly medical and nursing ones and relate to resuscitation and maintaining life, nutrition, and the prevention of limb contractions, skin ulceration and other complications of severe injury and immobilisation.

490 When people recover from coma, that state is always followed by a period of confusion which varies from being very brief to being very prolonged. People with the most severe injuries may never recover from confusion and others never emerge from coma. Confusion is frequently associated with agitation, aggression and a range of disinhibited behaviours. Management of this is particularly difficult on medical and surgical wards, especially when individuals are fully ambulant. Their transfer to acute psychiatric care or to a specialist brain injury rehabilitation unit can lead to much reduced use of sedative medications and this can have a beneficial effect upon longer-term rehabilitation. However, the staff of acute psychiatric wards are often reluctant to accept these patients for a variety of reasons.

491 When confusion resolves, the injured person may be left with a wide range of physical, cognitive and emotional problems. Usually, the most rapid improvement is in the first year after injury with a perceptible plateauing at around two years. The most enduring difficulties are usually in the realm of emotion, behaviour and cognition - the injured person is not the person he or she was. Some of these problems improve but others may worsen. In particular, the stress on a spouse, partner or family member may begin to tell. Commonly, relationships and living arrangements break down. Depression and even psychoses are much more common than in the general population, and the mental health of carers also suffers.

492 The longer term course and outcome is influenced particularly by the age of the person at the time of injury and the severity of injury. The loss of a significant amount of brain tissue in an older person can hasten the development of dementia. Epilepsy may develop, particularly after severe injury, as may hydrocephalus.

493   Each injured person's carer has much to cope with, from the shock of the injury itself, through coming to terms with the injured individual's disabilities, and their changed financial circumstances to, particularly, the loss of the person they formerly cared about.

494   Many different services and agencies may be involved and co-ordination of these different inputs is vital if the quality of service delivery is to be maintained and unnecessary duplications prevented.

495   Thus, the clinical tasks are many and varied. A specialist service that is designed specifically to meet the needs of brain injured people is best equipped to address these tasks, and care managers or co-ordinators are particularly effective in ensuring that individuals are able to make best use of existing services.

EARLY ONSET DEMENTIA

496   Usually, early onset dementia presents with a gradually worsening memory or change in personality. The GP is usually the first port of call. Full investigation and referral to a specialist may not take place immediately, because many emotional and stress-related factors can impair memory and alter temperament.

497   Initially, referral for investigation may be made to a wide range of specialists. Probably, neurologists are the specialists to whom people are most commonly referred when they are under the age of 65. Generally, neurologists see their role as diagnostic though, if there is the possibility of heritability, they may refer patients to a medical genetics department. If behaviour or emotional problems are very prominent, neurologists refer patients to the mental health services. Treatable and reversible causes of memory disorder and dementia will also be identified and treated.

498   There may follow a period of months or years during which the memory and skills of the individual gradually become more impaired, employment is lost and the burden of care becomes heavier and more continuous. Also the patient may show very marked emotional distress or aggression.

499   Restlessness, aimless wandering and impaired sleep are common. Ideally, the situation will be monitored by members of a primary healthcare team or by a specialist service and appropriate interventions made. These will vary depending upon the number of carers available (family members, neighbours, etc) and the severity of the problems. Some people with early onset dementia progress in a quiet, calm and undistressed way into a state of infant-like dependency. They are the exception. Medication, home care and sitting, daycare, respite care and occasional hospital care may all be needed. Eventually, nursing home care is necessary in the later and terminal stages, but this is not invariable.

500   Throughout all this, the needs of carers for support are great and usually increase with time. Their experience involves the gradual loss of their loved one, coupled with an increasingly demanding nursing role. Relinquishing care to a nursing home can be particularly distressing and guilt-provoking and can be delayed by improved levels of respite care and support.

HUNTINGTON'S DISEASE

501   The symptoms of Huntington's Disease may develop at any age from childhood to old age, but most people who have the disease develop overt indications of it in their fourth and fifth decades. Initial symptoms can include mild inco-ordination or chorea, personality changes or those of psychiatric disorder. Many families are aware of the diagnostic possibility because of the presence of an affected parent or sibling.

502   Usually, initial assessment is conducted by the person's GP with subsequent referral to a neurologist or psychiatrist. Diagnostic testing is now the norm.

503   In addition, there are increasing numbers of people who have had pre-symptomatic testing and they are aware that they will develop the disorder. These tests are carried out by departments of medical genetics and pre-symptomatic testing is generally associated with counselling and follow-up.

504   The long-term course of the disorder is variable, both with regard to the movement disorder that characterises the disease and changes in mental state. In a small proportion of people, there is no significant emotional change or psychiatric disorder beyond a slowing of thought and reduced communication. But in most cases there are psychiatric changes. Usually these changes can be improved by appropriate treatment which may require admission of the person to a psychiatric unit. Also, the severity of chorea can be greatly improved by medication.

505   In the later stages of the disease, there is usually impairment in speech articulation and problems can also occur with swallowing. Increasing inco-ordination may lead to the need for a wheelchair and assistance with feeding, bathing and toileting. Physiotherapy and speech and language therapy may be of some value in maintaining function. Cognitive impairment progresses as the disease advances, but the physical handicaps tend to overwhelm the presentation. Similarly, acute psychiatric problems tend to become less challenging in the late stages. Most patients require nursing home care in the terminal stages. Most often, death is caused by chest and urinary tract infections.

506   The clinical tasks in managing people with Huntington's Disease are also many and varied. Their performance is facilitated by staff having experience in managing others with the same disorder but, even then, can be challenging and unpredictable. Key workers are particularly important in supporting and monitoring patients at home, co-ordinating the different aspects of care, and providing a contact point at times of crisis.

THE ROLE OF PRIMARY HEALTHCARE TEAMS

507   Staff of primary healthcare teams (PHCTs) should retain the closest and most frequent contact with people who have these and other organic psychiatric disorders. But the relative rarity of these disorders means that each GP and other PHCT members will manage few of them during their working life, hence they are usually dependent upon key workers and specialist teams for advice and information. Therefore, good communication with specialist teams is important and this should be facilitated by proper and effective implementation of the Care Programme Approach.

The Implications for
Provider Managers

KEY COMMON FEATURES OF THE DISORDERS

508 Acquired brain injury, early onset dementia and Huntington's Disease have many clinical features in common. The range of impairments and disabilities is wide, spanning cognition, behaviour control and emotion, in addition to possible problems with movement and perception. In most cases the disabilities alter with increasing time and age, usually for the worse. The precise pattern in each individual is unique and the demands made on family members include those of coming to terms with the loss of the person they knew and a drastically altered role within their relationship. The response of children, parents and others can be both helpful and hurtful, particularly when the need to relinquish care is considered. Relatives spanning four generations have been known to attend care planning meetings.

509 Individual GPs, general psychiatrists, psychiatric nurses, social workers or members of the professions allied to medicine will encounter people with these conditions only occasionally and so may feel ill-equipped to deal with them. Therefore, it is sensible for a single individual and for a designated team to become the local experts in each district with the intention of their helping to educate each affected person's primary healthcare team. A common complaint made by carers is that they know more about their relative's condition, technically as well as practically, than the professionals with whom they deal.

510 Fortunately, existing generic and specialist mental health services contain the essential elements of care for these groups.

THE KEY PRINCIPLES OF EFFECTIVE SERVICES

511 There are many possible configurations of mental health services for these three client groups, but certain features are important if they are to be effective:

- good clinical leadership;

- comprehensive, expert and timely assessment, recurrent re-assessments and treatment;

- targeted multi-disciplinary work, with goal setting;

- good communication and collaboration between agencies, particularly health, social and education services and those in the non-statutory sector;

- well co-ordinated application of the Care Programme Approach and of care management;

- a range of care options with explicit and effective procedures for determining or sharing the core responsibility for continuing care;

- support and advocacy for service users;

- education, support and advice for carers;

- trained and experienced care managers and co-ordinators who are not allowed to become overburdened;

- good initial training of the professionals who have access to continuing professional development.

THE IMPLICATIONS FOR
PROVIDER MANAGERS

Clinical Leadership

512   Clinical leadership can come in many forms. Often, consultants in the specialties that follow may be involved.

- **Neuropsychiatry**

  Neuropsychiatry is a relatively new specialty within psychiatry. Recognised specialists have acquired their expertise by a variety of routes. Some deal with a wide range of neuropsychiatric conditions and run a service which supports people with these to varying extents. Others are involved in the management of a particular condition or conditions (eg epilepsy, brain injury etc). The British Neuropsychiatry Association is a well established body which organises conferences twice-yearly. The time may now be right for the Royal College of Psychiatrists to advise on the clinical responsibilities of the holders of neuropsychiatry posts and their training requirements.

- **Old Age Psychiatry**

  Old age psychiatrists have particular expertise in the diagnosis and management of dementia in older people and, in many parts of the country, they may also manage younger people with dementia, particularly in the late stages. This includes people in the later stages of Huntington's Disease, if cognitive impairment is a significant part of their disability.

- **The Psychiatry of Learning Disability**

  Psychiatrists who specialise in the learning disabilities manage mental health problems in people with learning disability, one cause of which may be brain injury prior to birth or in early infancy and childhood. While brain injury at an early stage of development often leads to a very different long-term outcome, there are similarities with brain injured adults and older children, and some problems are common in both circumstances, such as epilepsy. Therefore, it is not surprising that some consultants in this specialty have taken a particular interest in brain injury in adults and developed specialist services for this client group. However, brain injured adults and their families are often reluctant to become involved with generic learning disability services which they see as not being tailored to their needs.

- **General Adult Psychiatry**

  General adult psychiatrists manage people with all of these disorders but often only *in extremis*. Some provider agencies are able to identify a general psychiatrist who has taken a particular interest in one of these conditions, Huntington's Disease being the most common. Many general psychiatrists are willing to take on a sessional commitment to one of these patient groups, if their additional resource and training needs are addressed. The HAS has found that, generally, there is a high level of interest in neuropsychiatric problems.

- **Rehabilitation Psychiatry**

  In the past, consultants with expertise in psychiatric rehabilitation have managed people with each of these three conditions within long-stay beds. The great reduction in the number of these beds in recent years has resulted in these specialists becoming more reluctant to be involved. However, in one county, the rehabilitation consultant has developed an inpatient unit for people with Huntington's Disease and the service includes staff who provide support in the community.

- **Clinical Psychology**
  Clinical psychologists with special expertise in neuropsychology have taken a lead role in some districts, particularly in relation to brain injury services where rehabilitation, re-education and adjustment are key issues. These services tend to be community-based and function effectively, particularly where there is good liaison with the local or sector-based community mental health services.

The Care Programme Approach (CPA)

513 The Care Programme Approach has become a basic tool for mental health services in their delivery of effective and efficient services for people with severe and complex needs. It is proving effective in some districts in co-ordinating and shaping the care provided for people with mental health disorders in the context of organic brain disease.

514 As an example of good practice, the mental health service in North Warwickshire, which serves a population of approximately 180,000, has well developed Care Programme Approach procedures and information systems. The staff of services there were able to identify 16 users from these three client groups who were registered on their Care Programme Approach system and receiving regular monitoring (four with Huntington's Disease, four with acquired brain injury and eight with early onset dementia). This is a service which is largely general psychiatric in orientation and consultant staffing. In the main, these patients require complex care programmes by virtue of the complex mix of their social and health needs.

515 It is important to underscore the fact that the Care Programme Approach is applicable not only to people with schizophrenia and affective disorders but to anyone with severe mental health problems. The threshold for initiating a complex care programme will vary from provider to provider but the number cited from Warwickshire could be seen as providing a rule of thumb in assessing the current application of the Care Programme Approach to these three client groups.

EXISTING SERVICE MODELS AND APPROACHES TO SERVICE PROVISION

516 There is a limited range of existing services for the three client groups and so there is much room for innovation. Some examples of current mental health services for people with acquired brain injury, early onset dementia and Huntington's Disease are described below. The fieldwork conducted by the HAS found the staff involved in these services enthusiastic and keen to share their experience. All of the services have evolved and developed since their inception.

Inpatient Units and Other Clinical Services

Acquired Brain Injury

517 The neurobehavioural units in Stoke-on-Trent and Newcastle-upon-Tyne, and the brain injury units in Liverpool and Cardiff offer multi-disciplinary mental health care including assessment, treatment,

rehabilitation, and respite and crisis care. They are all managed by consultants with special responsibility for neuropsychiatry, though the unit in Cardiff has been developed within a learning disability service.

518   Shropshire, Nottingham and Worcestershire have community-based services for people with acquired brain injury that are managed in part by clinical psychologists.

Huntington's Disease

519   The Foxglove Unit at Mill Lodge, Kegworth, Leicestershire, is a residential unit for people with Huntington's Disease. It offers outreach services and respite and inpatient care within a mental health setting. The unit serves the county of Leicestershire. The unit is managed by a consultant with special responsibility for psychiatric rehabilitation who has a single session allocated to people with Huntington's Disease. The neuro-behavioural unit in Stoke-on-Trent includes up to three beds for people with mental health problems resulting from Huntington's Disease. More cognitively impaired people are managed by the Kingswood (neuropsychiatric high dependency) Unit which also serves the Stoke area. People with Huntington's Disease who are acutely psychotic may be admitted initially to the local unit for people with an acute mental illness. All are managed by a consultant with special responsibility for neuropsychiatry. Also, there is an assessment clinic conducted jointly with the supra-district genetic and the local neurology services for people seeking pre-symptomatic testing.

520   The service in Newcastle-upon-Tyne for people with Huntington's Disease includes responsibility for people in the whole of the former North East Region and there is a joint clinic with the former Regional Medical Genetics service. People may be admitted to designated beds on an acute mental illness or the neurobehavioural unit for assessment and treatment. The service is run by a consultant with special responsibility for neuropsychiatry who also has a liaison neuropsychiatry role to offer expert advice to the staff of a general hospital.

Early Onset Dementia

521   In Liverpool, a consultant with special responsibility for old age psychiatry has a designated weekly session for people with early onset dementia and there is a community team that specialises in caring for people in this client group.

522   In Stoke-on-Trent, the Kingswood Unit provides inpatient care for people with early onset dementia (caused by progressive degenerative disorders and severe single insult damage). The unit is managed by a consultant with special responsibility for neuropsychiatry.

523   Recently a similar inpatient unit has been opened in Shropshire and is managed by a consultant in old age psychiatry.

Memory and Cognitive Impairment Clinics

524   Over 20 clinics that are designated to offer services to people with memory and cognitive problems exist in the UK. The HAS has received details of the clinics provided in Leicester and Liverpool. Several memory clinics are attached to university academic departments and are a focus of research and, commonly, they offer very detailed and standardised evaluations of cognition and disability in the people who are referred. They tend to be well regarded by users as centres that

offer comprehensive expert assessment. At their best, they are linked closely with community follow-up and support services.

525 The most cost effective way of running clinics of this type is yet to be determined but a one stop-assessment, including interviews and investigations conducted on the same day, is emerging as the ideal. The Alzheimer's Disease Society has compiled a list of clinics of this kind. More general clinics run by other specialists, particularly neuropsychiatrists, old age psychiatrists and neurologists, include assessment of memory and cognitive disorders in people referred to them.

DEVELOPING NEW MENTAL HEALTH SERVICES FOR PEOPLE WITH BRAIN DISORDERS

526 The development of additional services for people with mental health problems as a result of brain disease is required. An adequate national network of services may only be achieved when each health authority works in conjunction with local providers to identify clinicians who are willing to be responsible for these patient groups, backed up by recognised specialists at supra-district centres that are able to offer advice and more specialised assessments. Nonetheless, it is important to emphasise that by no means all of the problems encountered by these patients and their carers require such a high level of expertise.

527 This review has focused upon three diagnostic groups because of the limitations of time and because the three groups included have the most pressing needs for service developments. People with epilepsy, Parkinson's Disease and a long list of other brain pathologies may also benefit from an increase in the experience and training of mental health professionals with neuropsychiatric disorders. Providers who have developed services of this kind have found that they attract extra-contractual referrals. There are also examples of the improved commissioning of these services, funded by existing payments to private sector providers, and there are opportunities for consortia of purchasing authorities to commission developments from interested local providers.

THE USE OF NON-STATUTORY SECTOR PROVIDERS

Private Sector Providers

528 Private sector services certainly have a role to play in the care of people with mental health problems as a result of these three types of disorder. Private hospital units are most used in the management of people with acquired brain injury. The specialist NHS units mentioned earlier may also refer cases to the private sector, particularly those who may benefit from more prolonged and rigorous behavioural approaches. It is likely, though, that commissioners who are able to contract with local providers for appropriate programmes of care for these groups will expend less on private sector placements.

529 Residential, hospital-based units have been in existence for over two decades in the private sector. More recent developments in private care have included care and case management services to co-ordinate care, provide support and advocacy. Presently, the insurers of accident victims are the heaviest users of these services.

Voluntary Sector Providers

530   The voluntary sector has been particularly effective in providing:

- daycare services;

- carer and user support;

- education; and

- advocacy.

The specialist services visited by the HAS in performing this review all had links with local voluntary sector organisations and providers. Links include the sessional involvement of community nurses and other staff in voluntary sector day units.

531   In many instances, the development of significant behaviour or emotional problems in people attending voluntary sector daycare makes their continued attendance difficult. Close liaison with the mental health services can help but, as in all forms of severe mental disorder, voluntary sector services should complement rather than substitute for statutory services.

Checklists and References

CHAPTER 16

CHECKLIST 1

THE COMMISSIONER'S CHECKLIST

1.	Do you know what mental health resources are presently deployed in the care of people with:	
	• acquired brain injury?	☐
	• Huntington's Disease?	☐
	• early onset dementia?	☐
2.	Do you have a strategy for improving existing or developing new services for people with these disorders?	☐
3.	Are you or have you considered collaborating with other commissioners in developing services for people in each of these client groups?	☐
4.	Do you have local providers with whom you are working, or could work, to achieve your strategy?	☐
5.	Do you have a forum where a strategy for service development in this area can be discussed and agreed with the senior staff of the social services departments?	☐
6.	Do you have an accurate or estimated knowledge of the prevalence of each of these disorders in your area?	☐
7.	Have you performed a needs assessment for people with these disorders?	☐
8.	Is the requirement for services for people with these disorders mentioned in your current mental health and other healthcare contracts?	☐
9.	Have you ascertained whether or not your local providers manage people with these disorders within the Care Programme Approach?	☐
10.	Have you canvassed local carers and users on their view of existing services?	☐
11.	Currently, do you have sufficient local expertise in the care of people with these disorders?	☐
12.	Does the medical genetics service you commission have links with clinical services, particularly those relating to Huntington's Disease?	☐
13.	Do you know how much you are currently spending on extra-contractual referral payments for people with these disorders?	☐
14.	Do you have contracts for a sufficient range of primary care, community-based and hospital based specialist services for people in each of the three client groups?	☐
15.	Do you monitor these contracts? And how do you do this?	☐
16.	Have you negotiated agreements for the referral of people on each of these client groups to very specialised services when necessary?	☐
17.	Are there very specialised services within the district?	☐
	If not, where is the nearest very specialised service for each client group?	☐

18. Is the knowledge-base within your organisation sufficient?	☐
19. Do you have an OD programme?	☐
20. Do you require your providers to make induction, basic level and continuing education available to their staff relating to these three client groups?	☐
Is this paid for within the contract price?	☐
21. Do you have a mechanism to promote inter-agency collaboration and one to resolve disputes over clinical and financial responsibilities between provider agencies?	☐

CHECKLIST 2

THE PROVIDER'S CHECKLIST

1.	Do you have a consultant who has a specialist role in managing any or all of the disorders of:	
	• acquired brain injury?	☐
	• Huntington's Disease?	☐
	• early onset dementia?	☐
2.	Have you considered seeking the establishment of such sessions/post?	☐
3.	Do you have other clinical staff or sessions targeted to the care of these groups?	☐
4.	Are you rigorously applying the Care Programme Approach to people with mental health problems as a result of:	
	• acquired brain injury?	☐
	• Huntington's Disease?	☐
	• early onset dementia?	☐
5.	Do you know how many patients with these disorders are the subject of:	
	• the CPA?	☐
	• the supervision register?	☐
	• supervised discharge?	☐
6.	Do you have a policy on hospital admissions for people with acute mental disorder who are also in one of these three client groups?	☐
7.	Do you have a policy on the care of people with AIDS-related dementia?	☐
8.	Do you have any formal or informal links with medical genetics services?	☐
9.	Do you have informal or formal working relationships with local non-statutory sector providers or carers groups (eg Headway, Huntington's Disease Association, Alzheimer's Disease Association)?	☐
10.	Please list local non-statutory sector providers here:	
11.	Do you have training programmes for:	
	• induction training of all staff?	☐
	• basic level training of all staff?	☐
	• continuing professional development?	☐

CHECKLIST 3

ACQUIRED BRAIN INJURY

Causes

HEAD TRAUMA	– Closed (the skull is not penetrated but the brain is shaken violently within the skull) – Open (the skull is penetrated)
HAEMORRHAGE	– Around the brain (extra-dural sub-arachnoid and sub-dural) – Inside the brain (intra-cerebral)
METABOLIC	– Due to severely reduced supply of oxygen to the brain (hypoxia) - caused by, for example, choking, carbon monoxide poisoning, cardiac arrest or drowning – Due to severely reduced supply of glucose (which is essential for metabolism) to the brain, for example, caused by insulin overdosage
NUTRITIONAL	– Due to lack of essential vitamins (usually in the context of general self-neglect and often associated with alcohol misuse)
INFECTION	– Due to viruses such as Herpes Simplex and HIV (encephalitis) – Due to bacteria (meningitis and brain abscess) – Due to fungal and other infections (usually in people with HIV or on immuno-suppressant drugs)
TOXIC	– Alcohol, heavy metals such as lead and solvents
OTHER	– eg thrombosis blocking the blood supply to the brain

CHECKLIST 4
POST-TRAUMATIC AMNESIA

Severity of PTA and Outcome

PTA	Severity	Expected Outcome
Up to 1 hr	Minor	Full recovery, although a small number of patients have prolonged and significant problems.
1 hr - 1 day	Moderate	Full recovery, but there may be problems (eg memorising and memory loss, irritability, emotional lability) for some months.
2-7 days	Severe	Eventually, most patients will make a full recovery, although this could take many weeks or months.
1-2 weeks	Very Severe	The chances of full recovery diminish with this severity of PTA. Recovery is likely to be slow (over many months), and often incomplete.
2-4 weeks	Extremely Severe	Greatly diminishing chances of full recovery.
> 4 weeks	Extremely Severe	Chances of complete recovery are extremely small. Most patients will have permanent and significant disabilities.

CHECKLIST 5

THE GLASGOW COMA AND SCALE OUTCOME

GCS Score Related to the Severity and Outcome from Brain Injury

GCS	Severity	Outcome
3-5	Very Severe	High risk of death. Those who survive will have permanent and significant disabilities
6-8	Severe	Most patients will survive but with a high probability of permanent and significant problems
9-12	Moderate	Eventual complete recovery for most patients but this may take many months and even then there may be residual problems
13-15	Minor	Rapid and complete recovery for most patients. Nonetheless, a small number will have significant and prolonged problems

CHECKLIST 6 (continued)

THE ANATOMY OF THE BRAIN

Side View of a Healthy Human Brain

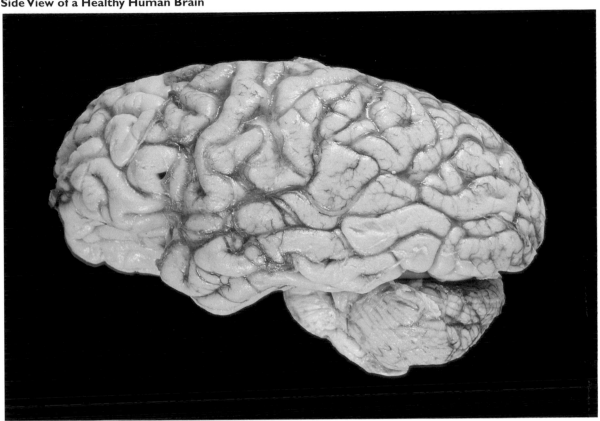

**The Left Hemisphere of the Brain,
Cerebellum and Brain Stem Viewed from the Left**

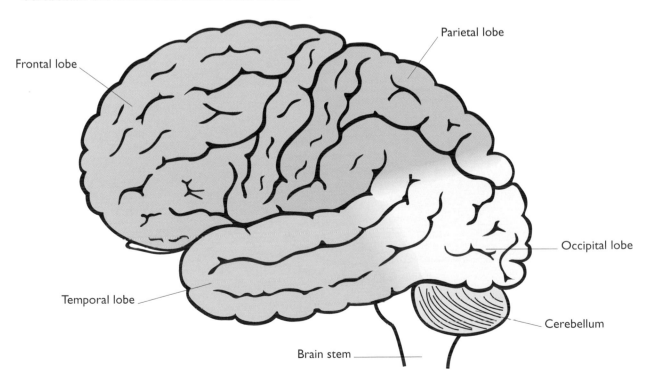

CHECKLIST 6 (continued)

THE ANATOMY OF THE BRAIN

Median (profile) Section through the Centre of a Whole Human Brain

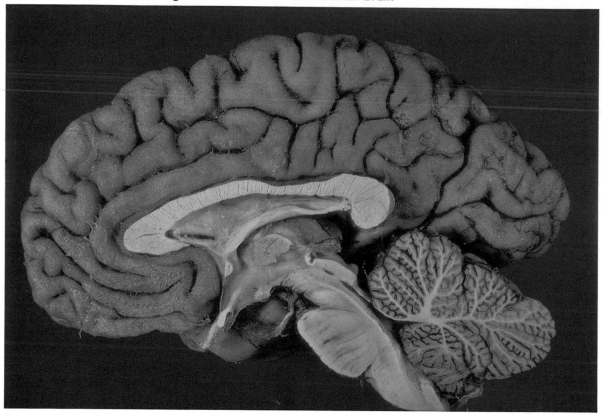

Internal Surface of the Right Hemisphere

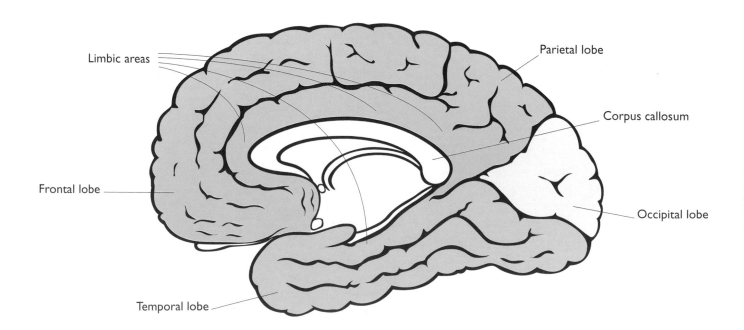

CHECKLIST 6 (continued)

THE ANATOMY OF THE BRAIN

**False-colour Nuclear Magnetic Resonance (NMR) Image
of an Axial Section through a Human Head showing a Normal Brain**

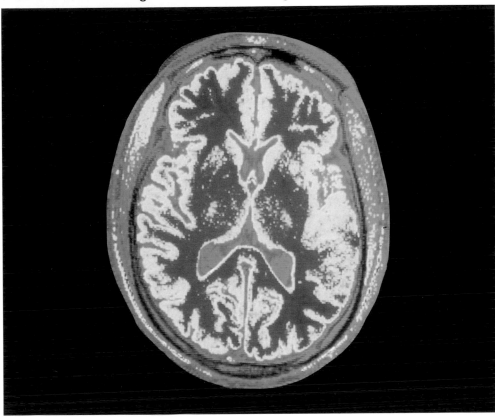

The Brain Viewed from Below

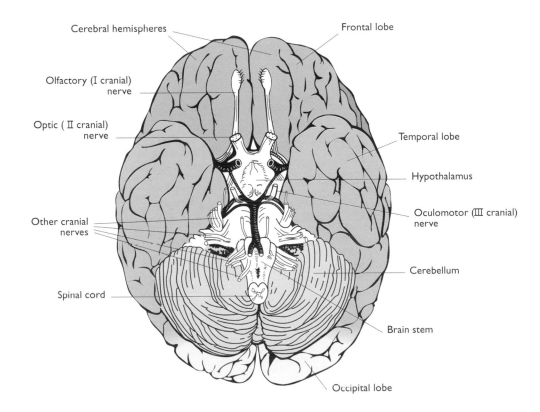

CHECKLIST 6 (continued)

THE ANATOMY OF THE BRAIN

**Coloured Magnetic Resonance Imaging (MRI) –
Median Sagittal Scan through a Human Head**

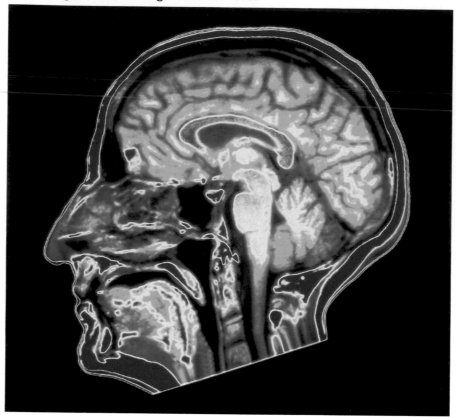

Diagram Indicating Some of the Structures Seen in the MRI Scan Above

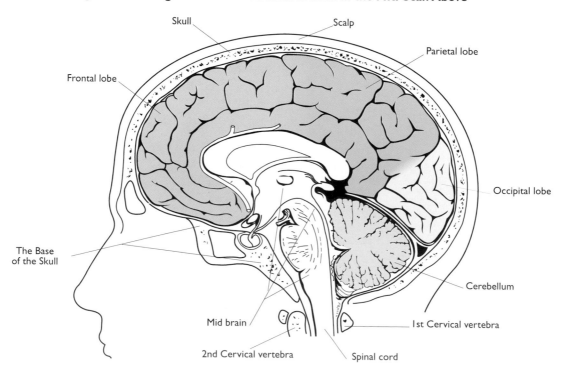

CHECKLIST 7

CAUSES OF DEMENTIA

- **Progressive Causes**
  - Alzheimer's Disease
  - Vascular (multiple infarction)
  - Pick's Disease and other lobar dementias
  - Lewy Body Disease
  - Huntington's Disease
  - Creutzfeldt-Jakob Disease (spongiform encephalopathy)
  - Infection (HIV, neurosyphilis)
  - Progressive supranuclear palsy
  - Wilson's Disease
  - Kuf's Disease
  - Demyelinating Disease

- **Dementia Due to Brain Damage**
  - Traumatic brain injury
  - Brain haemorrhage
  - Brain infection (meningitis and encephalitis)
  - Hypoxia and hypoglycaemia
  - Poisoning (lead and other heavy metals)
  - Alcohol misuse

- **Potentially Reversible Conditions that may Present as Dementia**
  - Hypothyroidism and other endocrine disorders
  - Drug toxicity
  - Liver and kidney failure (chronic)
  - Vitamin deficiencies (particularly B vitamins)
  - Hydrocephalus
  - Severe depression

CHECKLIST 8

EPIDEMIOLOGY

**The Prevalence of Disability after Acquired Brain Injury
(estimated for a 500,000 total population)**

Disorder	Prevalence	Remarks
TBI	625	Survivors after severe head injury with significant permanent disability
Stroke	235	People aged 35-64 inclusive

**The Prevalence of Dementia in Younger People
and Huntington's Disease
(estimated for a 500,000 total population)**

Disorder	Prevalence	Remarks
Dementia • DAT	40	People aged 45-64 years inclusive
• other degenerative dementias	26	People aged 45-64 years inclusive
	7	People aged <45 years (estimated)
• due to brain damage	25	People aged <65 years (estimated)
• Huntington's disease	50	Rates increase with the quality of the survey and this is the highest suggested prevalence

**The Prevalence Rates of other Neurological Conditions
that have Psychiatric Implications
(estimated for a 500,000 total population)**

Condition	Rate
Parkinson's disease (idiopathic)	500
Multiple sclerosis	500
Epilepsy	2,500

CHECKLIST 9

ACQUIRED BRAIN INJURY

A Summary of the Natural History and the Associated Needs of a Person after ABI

PHASE	DESCRIPTION	TYPES OF INTERVENTION REQUIRED (in order of priority)	COMMENTS
Acute Care	The phase of resuscitation, immediate care and initial medical and nursing treatment.	1 Medical, surgical, nursing, radiological intensive care and investigation. 2 Physiotherapy. 3 Social work.	The prime focus is on saving life and preventing or reducing complications. Physiotherapy is started, as soon as the patient is well enough, in order to reduce disabilities.
Rehabilitation	Rehabilitation is started as soon as patients are medically stable.	1 Occupational therapy, speech and language therapy, physiotherapy, neuropsychology. 2 Social work. 3 Medical, nursing.	The prime focus is on each patient's functional abilities and on reducing disabilities.
Community Care	Arrangements for community care should be initiated at the same time as rehabilitation begins.	1 Social work. 2 Community and volunteer agencies, such as Headway. 3 Neuropsychology. 4 Occupational therapy, speech and language therapy, physiotherapy. 5 Medical (eg GP).	The core aim is to set up a stable regime that offers effective, sensitively timed and responsive case management.
Longer-term Requirements Specialist Services 1 In Support of Long-term Living Arrangements	Long-term care facilities are needed by patients whose disabilities are too severe for independent living.	1 Social work. 2 Volunteer agencies, such as Headway, and housing associations.	These services provide close supervision in community settings. Their focus is on enhancing the quality and productivity of life.
2 Behavioural Rehabilitation	Behavioural rehabilitation is required by patients whose behaviour difficulties are so severe that they cannot be managed in a conventional rehabilitation unit.	1 Neuropsychology, neuropsychiatry, nursing. 2 Occupational therapy, speech and language therapy and physiotherapy.	These services focus on reducing the behaviour deficits that reduce the patient's options for rehabilitation and community placement.

CHECKLIST 10

HUNTINGTON'S DISEASE

A Summary of the Natural History and the Associated Needs of a Person with Huntington's Disease

PHASE	DESCRIPTION	TYPES OF INTERVENTION REQUIRED (in order of priority)	COMMENTS
Pre-symptomatic or Diagnostic Phase (prodromal)	People who are at risk are identified and diagnostic tests are offered.	1 Medical surveillance and support (genetics and neuropsychiatry). 2 Access to non-statutory sector services and support eg Huntington's Disease Association (HDA).	People at risk or those who are identified as carrying the gene, and their relatives, may need much support and counselling in this phase.
Early Symptomatic Care	Symptoms begin to appear. Patients who are under medical surveillance are readily diagnosed.	1 Medical, nursing and therapy treatment of physical symptoms and emotional and behaviour problems. 2 HDA – for information and support. 3 Social work and care management – to anticipate and plan for future care needs.	People not under medical surveillance may have months of uncertainty before a definitive diagnosis is made. In this phase, patients with HD should be managed by one specialist clinical team.
Deterioration	Symptoms worsen – particularly emotional and behavioural ones. Family members' needs for support and respite become important.	1 Medical, nursing and therapy, as above. 2 HDA, as above. 3 Social work – family support and access to respite beds.	Often, families can cope for extended periods, if they receive adequate support.
Long-term and Terminal Care	Severe dementia and physical disabilities develop.	1 Nursing and social care. 2 HDA. 3 Medical and therapy services, as above.	Now, the main focus is on the provision of long-term nursing and social care as the person deteriorates. The nursing and social care should be delivered by specialists who have experience of working with people who have HD.

CHECKLIST 11

EARLY ONSET DEMENTIA

A Summary of the Natural History and the Associated Needs of a Person with Early Onset Dementia

PHASE	DESCRIPTION	TYPES OF INTERVENTION REQUIRED (in order of priority)	COMMENTS
Symptomatic Care	Symptoms begin to appear and a definite diagnosis is established in this phase. The needs of patients and their families for care and support should be anticipated.	1 Medical – definitive diagnosis. 2 Social work – to anticipate care needs and help family. 3 Non-statutory sector agencies, particularly the Alzheimer's Disease Society (ADS).	The main issue is diagnosis. Future needs for care should be anticipated and plans made now. Alternative options for care should be identified and discussed with patients and families.
Deterioration	In this phase, symptoms worsen – particularly the emotional and behavioural ones. Families may have problems in coping.	1 Medical (GP) and therapy services and practice nursing. 2 ADS. 3 Social work.	Medical needs reduce in this phase. Nursing and social care needs increase – often patients require day centres and access to respite beds. Families require education and support – usually from the ADS, practice nurses, and social workers.
Long-term and Terminal Care	Deterioration is more severe in this phase. The patient's personality begins to fragment.	1 Social work, including the provision of long-term care, is required. 2 ADS. 3 Nursing care, conducted with medical supervision of the patient, is prominent together with diminishing inputs from physical therapists.	Now medical needs are much less. The main requirement is for adequate long-term nursing and social care. This is most effective when provided in close inter-disciplinary collaboration. Often, this needs to be delivered in a residential setting.

CHECKLIST 12

THE VIEWS OF USERS AND CARERS

Users and carers voice opinions that are consistent and which have similarities across the three diagnostic conditions considered in this report. The HAS considers that these have much wider application and the list below summarises and condenses the views of users and carers that were put to the HAS about the components and qualities of services that they value and wish to see maintained and/or developed.

- Advocacy
- Access to specialist services
- Accurate and early diagnosis and testing
- Availability of specialist aids and equipment
- Avoidance of institutionalisation
- Better understanding by employers
- Care programming
- Case management
- Community rehabilitation services
- Continuing care
- Continuing integration of care managed by a skilled, interested and trained general practitioner
- Continuity of care
- Daycare
- Development of more specialist centres of expertise and for training
- Encouragement and maintenance of independence
- Emotional support mechanisms for patients and their carers
- Expert assessment and accurate diagnosis
- Flexibility of service commissioning, purchasing and provision
- Genetic counselling and testing, when appropriate
- Information for employers and the public
- Practical support
- Recognition of the burden carried by partners, family members, friends and spouses
- Recognition of the importance and practicality of their views
- Residential respite care
- Respite care
- Safety and security
- Specialist rehabilitation services
- Support in gaining access to benefits
- Training for carers, when necessary
- Training for all relevant professionals
- Welfare services advice

CHECKLIST 13

STRATEGIC ISSUES

Issues That Have Significant Strategic Implications for Commissioning Services for People with Acquired Brain Injury, Huntington's Disease and Early Onset Dementia

- The importance of early diagnosis.

- The importance of early and forward-looking planning of care.

- The predictable course of the disease.

- The increasing dependency of most patients with Huntington's Disease and early onset dementia.

- The mixture of physical, emotional, behavioural and mental health challenges that are presented to service designers, service managers and practitioners.

- The long timespan during which individuals and their families are likely to require increasing but changing types of services.

CHECKLIST 13 (continued)

STRATEGIC ISSUES

Other Issues that have Implications for Service Strategy, Design and Management

- Clarity of purpose and vision are essential in planning services for people who have complex problems. This requires a designated leader who has expertise in this arena or is willing to acquire it. If necessary, advice may need to be sought from acknowledged experts in the field and from outside the district.

- Service planning should be based on comprehensive assessments of need. This may be based on national norms, but is much more accurate if local information is also obtained. It is important that an accurate estimation is made. Currently, most districts do not provide a satisfactory service for all three groups of people and they may not be aware of the shortfall.

- Service users and carers should be consulted in order to develop effective provision. Their opinions are important especially when considered alongside the views of professional experts. Service users should be seen as pivotal to the strategic development of services.

- People with any of these three types of disorder have a range of health and social care needs. They require a range of types of treatment and care that cross the boundaries between providers. Partnerships between the agencies involved should be encouraged in order that efficient and comprehensive services are delivered.

- Due to the multi-faceted nature of the problems presented by people in all three groups of disorder, a co-ordinated approach to their management is required. This can be delivered by a case or care management concept wherein each person is allocated a skilled and experienced member of staff who is responsible for planning and orchestrating a comprehensive package of care.

- Often patients need to use several services at one time, or to move through different services sequentially in the course of their disease. Ease of travel may be facilitated by ensuring that the various services recognise their links and actively collaborate.

- The highly specialised nature of the work required by people with these kinds of disorder means that staff need continuing training, supervision and support.

- Wide promulgation and promotion of services will allow those in need, and other providers, to know of their existence.

- It is important to recognise that attention to the needs of the patient continues after the acute stage of their management has been completed. Continuing surveillance, intervention and care are essential for patients and their carers.

- The highly specialised nature of their work may mean that professionals feel isolated from general services. Contact with centres of excellence and other people doing similar work can help to reduce professional parochialism.

CHECKLIST 14

COMMISSIONING MENTAL HEALTH SERVICES

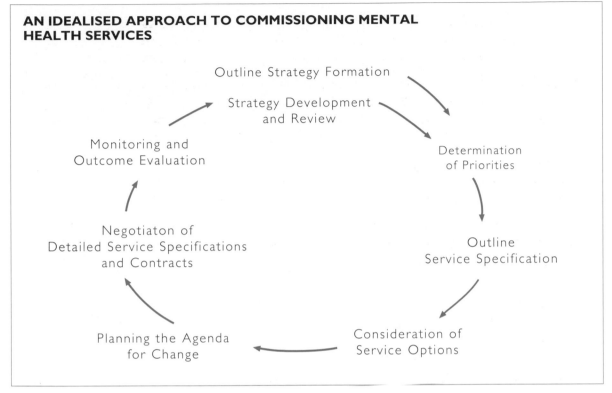

AN IDEALISED APPROACH TO COMMISSIONING MENTAL HEALTH SERVICES

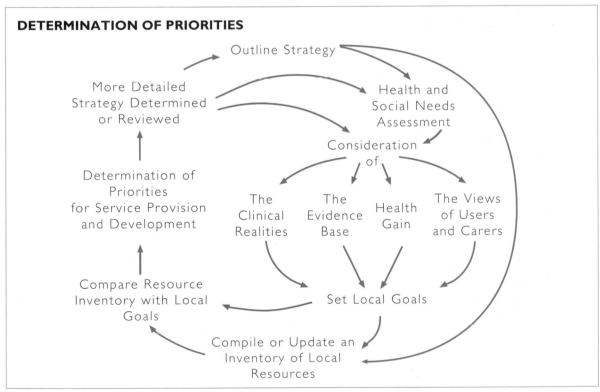

DETERMINATION OF PRIORITIES

CHECKLIST 15

A COMMISSIONING ACTION PLAN

Action Steps

1	Agree a multi-agency approach to services for people with: 　– acquired brain injury 　– Huntington's Disease 　– early onset dementia
2	Determine shared priorities
3	Map and audit current services
4	Develop an outline strategy
5	Assess need
6	Consider service options and plan an agenda for change
7	Negotiate service specifications and contracts
8	Monitor the results, including outcomes

CHECKLIST 16

A SUMMARY OF KEY ISSUES FOR THE COMMISSIONERS AND PURCHASERS OF SERVICES

GENERAL CONSIDERATIONS

Commissioners should:

• monitor trends in the incidence of the range of disorders;
 	
 • agree and implement a district-wide strategy, that:
 	
    − is agreed with the purchasers of services;
    − offers a clear continuum of help and support from the commissioners of other sectors of care and the appropriate purchasers of services;
 	
 • devise and implement a strategy specifically orientated to the needs of clients and carers;
 	
 • transcend organisational and funding boundaries.

KEY CONSIDERATIONS

Purchasing Services for People with ABI

Some key considerations include:
• know the nature, natural history, impacts and consequences (family, work and leisure) of disability in people who are brain injured;   • know where patients with ABI are likely to be, and how many of them there are within the district;   • be aware that, because of their other injuries, patients with TBI may be dealt with in orthopaedic or general surgical wards where their brain injuries and their longer-term consequences may be missed, or given insufficient attention;   • have a clear statement of what is wanted from each service provider. Be clear about this and avoid perverse incentives that stem from double messages. For instance, if quality targets are multiple (eg effective medical treatment such that skin ulcers are avoided; maximum functional improvement in daily living skills; reduction in number of hours of care; or speedy return to work), there is the possibility of some of these pulling the therapeutic processes in the same or, at times, conflicting directions;   • integrate the roles and work of the statutory (health, social, housing and education services) and non-statutory services (Headway and others).

CHECKLIST 16 (continued)

Purchasing Services for People with Huntington's Disease

Some key considerations include:
• know the nature, natural history, impacts and consequences (family, work and leisure) of disability in people who have Huntington's Disease;   • know where patients with Huntington's Disease are likely to be, and how many of them there are within the district;   • integrate genetic counselling and neuropsychiatric services;   • anticipate long-term care needs and plan service responses from the time when the diagnosis is made;   • integrate the roles and work of the statutory and non-statutory services.

Purchasing Services for Younger Patients with Dementia

Some key considerations include:
• know the nature, natural history, impacts and consequences of early onset dementia;   • know where patients with early onset dementia are likely to be, and how many of them there are within the district;   • integrate the roles and work of the statutory and non-statutory services;   • ensure that effective multi-disciplinary assessment facilities are available and clearly identified;   • ensure that the assessment services communicate clearly with the services that provide continuing care;   • be clear about who is providing mental health services for this client group and for their carers;   • anticipate future care and nursing needs and plan service responses to meet them once the diagnosis is established.

CHECKLIST 17

THE INTEGRATION OF THE SECTORS OF CARE

THE INTEGRATION OF THE SECTORS OF CARE

Mental Health Services

Social Services

Voluntary Sector Services

Acute Health Services

Other Services eg Housing, Criminal Justice

Tier 1

Tier 2

Tier 3

Tier 4

Hypothetical pathway of a person with a brain injury through integrated services

Arrows show a sample of possible referral and collaborative relationships

CHECKLIST 18

THE KEY PRINCIPLES OF EFFECTIVE SERVICE DELIVERY

There are many possible configurations of mental health services for these three client groups, but certain features are important if they are to be effective:

- clinical leadership;

- comprehensive, expert and timely assessment, recurrent re-assessments and treatment;

- multi-disciplinary working, with goal setting;

- good communication and collaboration between agencies, particularly health, social and education services and those in the non-statutory sector;

- application of the Care Programme Approach;

- a range of care options with explicit and effective procedures for determining or sharing the core responsibility for continuing care;

- support and advocacy for service users;

- education, support and advice for carers;

- trained and experienced care managers and co-ordinators who are not allowed to become overburdened;

- good initial training of the professionals and access to continuing professional development.

BIBLIOGRAPHY AND REFERENCES

Alzheimer's Disease Society, (1993). *Declaration of rights for younger people with dementia and their carers.* The Younger Person with Dementia. Alzheimer's Disease Society.

Bailey V, (1995). *Personal communication.*

British Medical Association and Law Society, (1995). *Assessment of mental capacity: guidance for doctors and lawyers.* London, BMA.

Brooks N, McKinlay W, Symington C, Beattie A, Campsie L, (1987). *Return to work within the first seven years of severe head injury.* Brain Injury, 1, 5-19.

Brooks N, (1990). *The head injured family.* Journal of Clinical & Experimental Neuropsychology, 13 (1), 1-34.

Brown P, (1996). *Bovine Creutsfeldt-Jakob disease?* British Medical Journal, 312, 791-792.

Butler Lord, (1975). *Report of the committee on mentally abnormal offenders, CMND 6244.* London, HMSO.

CARF - The Rehabilitation Accreditation Commission, (1996). *Standards Manual and Interpretive Guidelines for Medical Rehabilitation.* Tucson, Arizona.

Cox S, McClennan J, (1994). *A guide to early onset dementia.* University of Stirling.

CRAC - Council of Relatives to Assist in the Care of Dementia, (June 1994). *Early onset dementia: a living bereavement: the wife's story.*

Dayer A, Woodhouse K, (1993). *Prospects for pharmacological therapy of memory disorders.* Care of the Elderly, 5, 436.

DeArmond S J, Prusiner S B, (1995). *Etiology and pathogenesis of prion disease.* American Journal of Pathology, 146, 785-811.

Denys P, Azouvi P, Denormandie P, Samuel C, Patel A, Bussel B, (1996). *Late cognitive and behavioural improvement following treatment of disabling orthopaedic complications of a severe closed head injury.* Brain Injury, 10, 149-153.

Department of Health and Social Security, (1976). *A review of the Mental Health Act 1959.* London, HMSO.

Department of Health and Social Security, (1987). *Claims and payments regulations (1987).* Reg 33. London, HMSO.

Department of Health, Welsh Office, (1993). *Mental Health Act 1983: Code of Practice, laid before Parliament pursuant to Section 118(4) of the Mental Health Act 1983 (revised edition).* London, HMSO.

Department of Health, (1995). *Practical guidance on joint commissioning for project leaders.* London, Department of Health.

Department of Health, (1995). *Introduction to joint commissioning.* London, Department of Health.

Editorial, (1993). *Neuroepidemiology in the United Kingdom.* Journal of Neurology, Neurosurgery, and Psychiatry, 56, 733-738.

Enduring Powers of Attorney Act 1985. London, HMSO.

Finlayson M A J, Garner S H, (1994). *Brain injury rehabilitation: clinical considerations.* Williams & Wilkins, Baltimore.

Folstein M F, Folstein S E, McHugh P R, (1975). *Mini mental state.* Journal of Psychiatric Research, 12, 189-198.

Francis J, (1996). *Across the barriers: a report about Crofton Mews.* Community Care, February 1996.

Greenwood M, Walsh K, (1995). *Supporting carers in their own right.* Journal of Dementia Care, 3, 14-16.

Gururaj G, Satishchandra P, Subbakrishna D K, (1995). *Epidemiologic correlates of stroke mortality - observations from a tertiary institution.* Neurology India, 3, 29-34.

Harper P S, (1991). *Huntington's Disease.* London, W B Saunders.

Huntington's Disease Association Newsletter, (1995). London. Issue 48, 47-49.

King M, (1985). *Alcohol abuse in Huntington's Chorea.* Psychological Medicine, 15, 815-820.

Kitwood T, Bredin K, (1992). *Towards a theory of dementia care: personhood and wellbeing.* Ageing and Society, 12, 269-287.

Law Commission, (1995). *Mental incapacity, Law Commission No 231.* London, HMSO.

Maj M, (1990). *Organic mental disorders in HIV-1 infection.* AIDS, 51, 831-840.

Marsden C D, Fahn S, (eds), (1982). *Movement disorders.* New York, Butterworth Scientific.

Mattson B, (1974). *Huntington's Chorea in Sweden II. Social and clinical data.* Acta Psychiatrica Scandinavica, Suppl 255, 221-263. (Abstract).

McKeith I G, Perry R H, Fairbairn A F, Jabeen S, Perry E K, (1992). *Operational criteria for senile dementia of Lewy body type (SDLT) including the description of a neuroleptic sensitivity syndrome.* Psychological Medicine, 22 (4), 911-922.

Medical Disability Society, (1988). *The report of the working party on the management of traumatic brain injury.*

Mental Health Act 1983. London, HMSO.

Mental Health Act Code of Practice (1993). London, HMSO.

Newens A J, Forster D P, Kay D W K, Kirkup W, Bates D, Edwardson J, (1993). *Clinically diagnosed presenile dementia of the Alzheimer type in the Northern Health Region: ascertainment, prevalence, incidence and survival.* Psychological Medicine, 23, 631-644.

Newens A J, Forster D P, Kay D W K, (1995). *Dependency and community care in presenile Alzheimer's disease.* British Journal of Psychiatry, 166, 777-782.

NHS and Community Care Act 1990. London, HMSO.

NHS Executive, (1994). *EL(94)79, Towards a primary care-led NHS.* Department of Health.

NHS Executive, (1996). *LASSL(96)16/HSG(96)6, An audit pack for the Care Programme Approach.* Department of Health.

NHS Health Advisory Service, (1995). *A place in mind: commissioning and providing mental health services for people who are homeless.* London, HMSO.

NHS Health Advisory Service, (1995). *Together we stand - the commissioning, role and management of child and adolescent mental health services.* London, HMSO.

NHS Health Advisory Service, (1996). *The substance of young needs - commissioning and providing services for children and young people who use and misuse substances.* London, HMSO.

NHS Health Advisory Service, (1996). *Suicide prevention - the challenge confronted.* London, HMSO.

NHS Management Executive, (1993). *Purchasing for health.* The Health Publications Unit, Heywood, Lancs.

Pattie A, Gilleard C, (1979). *The manual of the Clifton assessment procedures for the elderly.* London, Hodder and Stoughton.

Powell T, (1994). *Head injury: a practical guide.* Winslow Press, Bicester.

Prasher V P, (1995). *Prevalence of psychiatric disorders in adults with Down's Syndrome.* The European Journal of Psychiatry, 9, 77-82.

Prasher V P, (1995). *Age-specific prevalence, thyroid dysfunction and depressive symptomatology in adults with Down's Syndrome and dementia.* International Journal of Geriatric Psychiatry, 10, 25-31.

Rosenthal M, Griffith E R, Bond M R, Miller J D, (1990). *Rehabilitation of the adult and child with traumatic brain injury (2nd Ed).* Philadelphia, F A Davis.

Shakespeare J, Anderson J, (1993). *Huntington's disease: falling through the net.* Health Trends, Vol 25, no 1, 19-23.

Sheffield Health, (1995). *Draft purchasing strategy for services for younger people with dementia.* Sheffield Health Commission.

Sperlinger D, Furst M, (1994). *The service experiences of people with presenile dementia: a study of carers in one London borough.* International Journal of Genetic Psychiatry, 9, 47-50.

Tate R L, Lulham J M, Bore G A, Strettles B and Pfaff A, (1989). *Psychosocial outcome for the survivors of severe blunt head injury: the results from a consecutive series of 100 patients.* Journal of Neurology, Neurosurgery and Psychiatry, 52, 1128-1134.

Thorvaldson P, Asplund K, Kuulasmaa K, Rajakangas A M, Schroll M, (1995). *Stroke incidence, case fatality, and mortality in the Who Monica project.* Stroke, 26, 361-367.

Watt D C, Seller A, (1993). *A clinico-genetic study of psychiatric disorder in Huntington's Chorea.* British Medical Journal, 306 (Suppl 23), 1-46.

Welsh Affairs Committee, (1995). *Severe head injuries: rehabilitation.* Third Report, Volume 1. London, HMSO.

Williams D D R, (1995). *Services for younger sufferers of Alzheimer's disease.* British Journal of Psychiatry, 166, 699-700.

Williams R, Avebury K, (1995). *A place in mind: commissioning and providing mental health services for people who are homeless.* NHS Health Advisory Service, London, HMSO

Williams R, Gay M, (1996). *The substance of young needs - commissioning and providing services for children and young people who use and misuse substances.* NHS Health Advisory Service, London, HMSO.

Williams R, Morgan H G, (1996). *Suicide prevention - the challenge confronted.* NHS Health Advisory Service, London, HMSO.

Williams R, Richardson G, (1995). *Together we stand - the commissioning, role and management of child and adolescent mental health services.* NHS Health Advisory Service, London, HMSO.

World Health Organisation, (1992). *The ICD-10 classification of mental and behavioural disorders.* World Health Organisation, Geneva.

THE ORIGINS OF THE REVIEW

1   This thematic review of mental health services for people with acquired brain injury, Huntington's Disease and early onset dementia is one of a series of thematic reviews prepared by the NHS Health Advisory Service (HAS).

2   The underlying aim of the review is to highlight the mental health needs of groups of people who had always been the concern of psychiatric services but whose needs are all too frequently less than optimally met.

3   This group includes people who have a wide range of diagnoses but, in order to better focus the review and simplify the fieldwork, three client groups were chosen for particular scrutiny. These three are the largest separate diagnostic groups within the field of brain disease and those for which there is wide recognition that relevant services could and should be improved. In this respect, they also have emblematic standing for people who have many other diagnoses. Indeed, any improvement in local services for people who have one of these diagnoses is likely, through the increased awareness of commissioners and purchasers and the expanded expertise of local providers, to have spin-off effects on the care provided for people with other brain diseases.

4   Dementia has many causes and associations and some of these (eg demyelinating disease, Parkinson's Disease) were not considered specifically in the review. Also, one of the most prevalent of the neurological diagnostic groups, that of epilepsy, was not included in this work. A key issue in relation to services for people with epilepsy concerns the question of which discipline should take principal responsibility for the long-term management of sufferers. Despite the strong associations of psychiatric disorder with epilepsy and the undoubted expertise of mental health staff who are also trained epileptologists, it is unlikely that the principal service providers for these people will be the mental health services. However, any service which improves its provision for the three diagnostic groups considered here must necessarily increase the local expertise in epilepsy management as this is a common associated problem in people with brain injury and early onset dementia.

5   The matter of signal importance in considering the output from the work done in conducting this review is to understand that the three diagnostic groups were chosen to illustrate issues of principle. It is these principles that resonated in the work of the HAS and, throughout this report, that should be the main consideration of readers. The circumstances of a significant portion of the population would be greatly improved if the broad principles identified in this report were applied. People with a much broader range of conditions, that also impact on physical capacity and intellectual functioning, as well as on emotional and behavioural experiences of life, and thereby powerfully impact on relationships, would also benefit from similar approaches to service design and delivery.

CONDUCTING THE REVIEW

6   At the outset of this review, the Director of the HAS established an expert advisory group to advise him. The first stage in this was the appointment of a leader and clinical co-ordinator drawn from the NHS who helped the Director to select other members of the committee.

7   Appointments were made to this group in order to include the key sectors of care and the key professional disciplines as well as individuals who have particular expertise with people in the chosen diagnostic groups.

8   Then, a review of the literature was conducted and six sites were identified for fieldwork visits. These included sites:

- where there was no established specialist service for people with the selected disorders but a developed capacity in offering the care programme approach;

- with a well established service for people with early onset dementia and a unit within a mental health setting for people who have brain injury;

- with a well established service for people diagnosed with Huntington's Disease, including a residential unit that specialises in caring for this group of people, and an academically-based memory clinic;

- with a well established district service for people with Huntington's Disease and a brain injury unit in a mental health setting;

- with a unit in a mental health setting for people who have a brain injury and a well-established service offering rehabilitation medicine; and

- with a unit in the setting of a learning disability service for people who have had a brain injury.

9   In addition, information was obtained on other relevant services which could not, due to limitations of time, be visited.

10   Prior to conducting the visits, a questionnaire was drawn up to determine the scope and range of current and planned services for these groups. This was sent to local commissioners, purchasers and providers prior to each visit. The visits included interviews with health commissioners and providers, the staff of social services departments, and with users and carers. During the visits, some of the principal questions posed were:

- what service is available within the mental health, and social services, and within the voluntary and private sectors for people with problems that place them within each of the three chosen diagnostic groups?

- do services for people in these groups feature in the local mental health strategy?

- how are the local services viewed by users and carers?

- is the care programme approach being applied to people with these diagnoses?

11   After the service visits had been completed, the review team (that was drawn from the steering committee) drew together the findings from the literature review that was conducted concurrently with the information gained during the fieldwork and views expressed in other submissions. This led to the development of the strategic approach to commissioning and providing services for people who are diagnosed

with one of the conditions in the three selected groups.

12 Finally, this report was drafted by members of the Director's expert advisory committee.

13 Figure 11 summarises the methodology for the review on which this document reports.

Figure 11

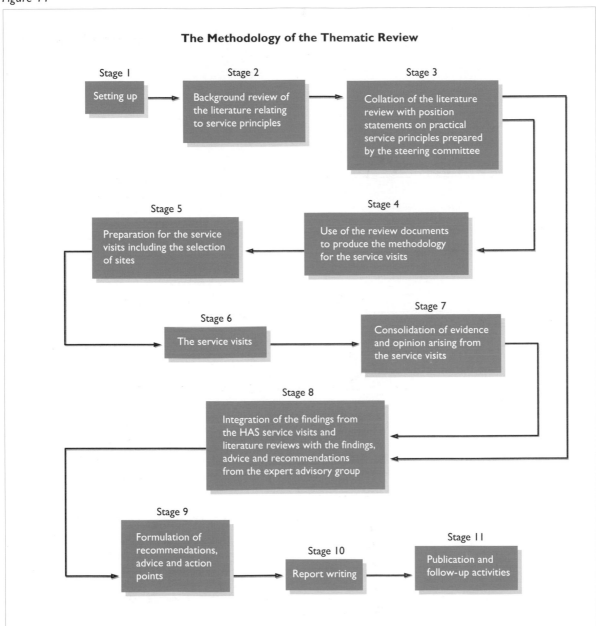

A- and Dys-

Many terms begin with the prefixes *a-* or *dys-*. A- literally means a complete inability to perform while *dys-* means an impaired ability. For example, amnesia should mean total loss of memory whereas dysmnesia would mean a partial loss of memory. However, the terms tend to be used loosely to the extent that the prefix A- is often used to indicate impaired ability as well as complete inability.

Affect

This is a term relating to a person's emotional disposition. Thus appropriate affect means that the individual shows emotional reactions that are appropriate in all the circumstances. Flattened affect means that little emotional response is made and that this is not appropriate. This is common after injury to the brain.

Akinesia

This means the inability to begin a movement or slowness in conducting it.

Amnesia

Amnesia means absence or loss of memory. Associated with head injury are retrograde amnesia and post-traumatic amnesia (see below). Amnesic patients may remember well events that are long past but be unable to remember recent events.

Anoxia

Anoxia is the term for failure of oxygen supply to an organ. The brain is very sensitive to lack of oxygen. Anoxic damage to the brain may occur as a result of injury to the head or arise, indirectly, as a consequence of other injuries, especially those to the chest and the circulation that cause interruption of the oxygen supply by failure of the gas to enter the body and/or failure of its passage in the blood to the brain.

Anti-convulsants

These are drugs which are taken to control epilepsy. Sometimes, they are prescribed prophylactically where the risk of epilepsy is calculated to be high. In general, the dosage is critical in order to achieve proper control yet avoid undue side-effects such as diminished powers of concentration. Alcohol intake should be minimal for patients on these drugs as the two may interact to make the effect of the drugs and the intensity of the side-effects unpredictable.

Anxiety

Anxiety is a natural reaction to doubts about one's future health and prosperity. Patients with impairments and disabilities, and their relatives, may well suffer from some degree of anxiety. Very high levels of anxiety are found in post-traumatic stress disorder.

Aphasia

Aphasia means the inability to use and/or understand language. This is not an inability to articulate words (that is called dysarthria) but is an inability to find the appropriate words and/or to decode the meaning of words. There are many forms, including expressive aphasia in which the ability to find and utter words is damaged. Usually, it is associated with damage to Broca's area. In receptive aphasia, the ability to understand words and also to monitor speech is damaged resulting in what is termed fluent or jargon aphasia. This kind of aphasia is usually associated with damage to Wernicke's area of the brain.

Ataxia

This term describes unsteadiness of gait resulting from defective control of muscles.

Broca's Area

Broca's area is the part of the brain (left posterior frontal cortex) that is responsible for the production of speech.

Cerebral Hemispheres

The cerebral hemispheres form the upper and largest part of the brain. The two hemispheres are the areas involved with higher mental ability and are essential in regulating the emotions.

Closed Head Injury

The great majority of civilian head injuries are closed ones. These are injuries in which the head has undergone a rapid change in velocity and, therefore, has been severely shaken about. The skull has not been penetrated and injury results from movement of the brain or the impact of increased pressure within the closed rigid box formed by the skull. It should be distinguished from penetrating head injury in which the skull is penetrated by a missile (eg bullet, shrapnel or other flying object).

Coma

This is the term that describes deep unconsciousness. In order to make the definition more precise, Jennett and Teasdale have offered the definition: *"not obeying commands, not uttering words, and not opening the eyes."* This is now generally used. In the Glasgow Coma Scale (GCS), total scores range from 3 (least responsive) to 15 (most responsive). No score discriminates absolutely patients in coma from those not in coma. However, 90% of patients who have a total 8 or less lie within the definition of coma. Patients whose individual scores total 9 or more do not have clinical evidence of coma. Therefore, 8 is usually taken as the GCS total score that demarcates being and not being in a coma.

CT Scan

The CT scan (computerised axial tomography) is a key investigation for head injured people. If there is reason to suspect intracranial injury or complications, particularly the formation of a haematoma, a CT scan of the head (sometimes called a brain scan) should be carried out. This provides a three dimensional picture by means of a succession of two dimensional X-ray pictures and indicates the position and extent of any haematoma. The early detection of haematoma, and, if appropriate, its urgent removal by operation, are key elements in reducing mortality and morbidity following head injury. However, the value of the CT scan must not be overestimated. For example, it cannot detect the diffuse microscopic damage which is characteristic of closed head injury and an apparently normal CT scan does not imply that the brain is necessarily normal.

Care Management

This concept arises from the NHS and Community Care Act 1990. It is a term used by social services departments to describe the process by which care in the community is organised, paid for, and delivered. It should ensure that the individual needs of both users and their carers are assessed, that the packages of care designed to meet those individual needs are arranged and that each programme is reviewed.

Care Programme Approach (CPA)

The CPA is intended to ensure continuing aftercare for the users of specialist mental health services, ie that they should not be lost to care.

Case Management

This concept arises from the NHS and Community Care Act 1990. It is a means of maximising the likelihood of successful treatment and community re-entry and describes a process in which each patient has a guide, advocate, organiser of therapeutic resources, and clinical manager. Case managers should ensure that each patient's needs are identified, resources are found and deployed, goals set and tracked and quality monitoring maintained.

Depressed Mood

A depressed mood is how people feel when they experience a persistent feeling of gloom. In such a state, individuals may take little pleasure in life and participate in few activities. It can be a persistent state, although it is less severe than a full depression in which a persistently depressed mood is associated with other key features.

Depression

In depression or depressive illness, there is a feeling of gloom, hopelessness, and a lack of conviction that one can act effectively. The presence of some or all of the following experiences is characteristic: loss of appetite; loss of libido; diurnal variation of mood; feelings of worthlessness; feelings of guilt; and suicidal intent.

Diffuse Axonal Injury

This is the term to describe widespread and patchy shearing of the axons (nerve cells) which interconnect areas of the brain. Damage of this kind is characteristic of what happens in the brain as a result of severe closed head injury.

Disinhibition

Disinhibition means behaviour that is socially inappropriate including anger, boastfulness and, possibly, swearing and inappropriate sexual advances.

Disorientation

This term may be used in two different ways:

- first, it may mean not being fully aware of one's location in time and place. Following head injury, disorientation in time and place is an indication that new information is not being properly registered, and this means that such a patient is still in the state of post-traumatic amnesia;

- left-right disorientation is a confusion between left and right.

Dys-

See *A- and Dys-*.

Dysarthria

This term is used to describe impairment of the ability to pronounce words (to be distinguished from dysphasia - see below).

Dysmnesia

Dysmnesia means impairment of memory. Dysmnesic patients may remember well events that are long past but have difficulty in remembering recent events.

Dysphasia

Dysphasia is the term meaning an impairment of the ability to use and/or understand language. Strictly, this is a lesser degree of impairment than aphasia, but, otherwise, a similar description applies.

Dyspraxia

Dyspraxia means impairment of the ability to carry out actions such as dressing or copying a shape. Strictly, this is a less severe form of apraxia.

Encephalitis

Encephalitis describes a pathological process or situation in which there is inflammation of the tissues that form the brain.

Encephalopathy

This is a general term to indicate that there is a disorder of brain function.

Focal

A deficit is said to be focal if the pattern of the symptoms and signs imply that there is local rather than generalised brain damage that could be causing the findings. Thus, the focal neurological deficit of right hemiparesis implies damage to the left motor strip or its associated nerve fibres and the focal neuropsychological deficit of poor verbal memory implies damage to the dominant (usually left) temporal lobe. There are other contrasting patterns of deficit (eg generalised dementia) which imply generalised brain damage. Recognition of focal symptoms and signs may help doctors to determine which part of the brain has been most severely damaged by a brain injury.

Frontal Lobe

The frontal lobe is the front part of the brain. It may be divided into the dorsolateral and orbito-medial areas and the motor strip. The first two make up most of the frontal lobe and damage to it give rise to the major frontal symptoms. The characteristic function of the frontal lobes is to drive and monitor behaviour. While other parts of the brain are concerned with understanding incoming information from the sense organs, the frontal lobes are responsible for:

- driving outputs - eg for attention to task, for get up and go;

- regulating outputs - eg for ensuring social and sexual behaviour is appropriate to the social situation or context.

Frontal Lobe Syndrome

The frontal lobe syndrome has a number of elements including:

- loss of attention to task, manifested as perseveration, and is related to damage to the dorsolateral frontal areas;

- loss of inhibition which results in outbursts of temper, and inappropriate social and sexual behaviour and is related to damage to the orbito-medial frontal areas.

GCS

See Glasgow Coma Scale.

Glasgow Coma Scale (GCS)

The GCS is used throughout the western world to measure and compare levels of responsiveness and to define coma and the severity of head injury. (For further information see Annex D).

Glasgow Outcome Scale (GOS)

The GOS is used throughout the western world and beyond to quantify the outcome of head injury. (For further information see Annex D).

GOS

See Glasgow Outcome Scale.

Haematoma

This is the term for a collection of clotted blood. The rapid expansion of a blood clot within the skull can cause severe and escalating brain damage and death. The great majority of those patients who are conscious after an initial blow but subsequently die (so called talk and die cases) do so because they have developed haematomas.

Hydrocephalus

Colloquially, this is referred to as water on the brain. When an excess of cerebro-spinal fluid becomes trapped inside the ventricles of the brain it compresses brain tissue by pushing it outwards. This is potentially very damaging and may occur as a complication after head injury.

Infarct

This term means that an area of tissue (eg brain tissue) is dead or damaged. This may result from lack of oxygen supply to the tissue due to an event which causes blockage or spasm of a blood vessel.

Inhibition

This is the term used to indicate the damping down of basic reactions, so that socially acceptable behaviour is maintained. Disinhibited patients may be prone to angry outbursts for little cause, boastfulness, swearing in inappropriate situations and unacceptable sexual advances.

Intracranial Pressure

Simply, intracranial pressure (ICP) is the pressure within the skull. A full understanding of how the pressure is regulated and of the impacts of high or low ICP is very complicated. But, ordinarily, the ICP is related to the pressure of the arterial blood as it enters the skull to supply the brain. Because the skull is rigid, the entry of blood at arterial pressure results in there being a normal level of pressure inside. The intracranial pressure may rise after head injury if there is swelling in the brain tissue due to the injury, if blood vessels are sheared resulting in an ooze of blood from tiny vessels, if a haematoma is formed from blood loss from damaged larger vessels and if cerebro-spinal fluid is unable to leave the skull due to blockage of a duct. A rise in intracranial pressure can have serious consequences as it may reduce the supply of blood to the brain, thereby reducing the supply of oxygen and nutrients. It may also further damage the brain by applying force on the tissues or pinch the nerves that run inside the skull between the brain tissue and bony prominences on the inside surface of the skull.

Figures 12a and b show two views of the inside of the skull. Both illustrate these bony prominences. Readers are referred to Figure 1d on page 20 to see the cranial nerves that come from the underside of the brain. A unilateral dilated pupil may be a gross sign of rising or raised ICP. It may occur due to the oculomotor nerve being pinched between a swollen brain and the bony prominences of the base of the skull.

Figure 12a **The Skull - A View Showing the Inside of the Base of the Skull**

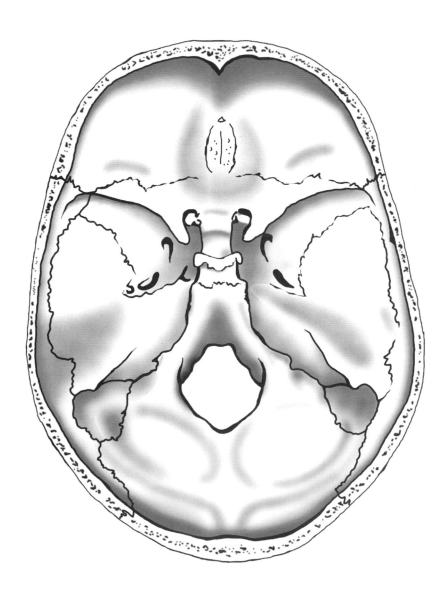

Figure 12b **The Skull - A Half-Side View**

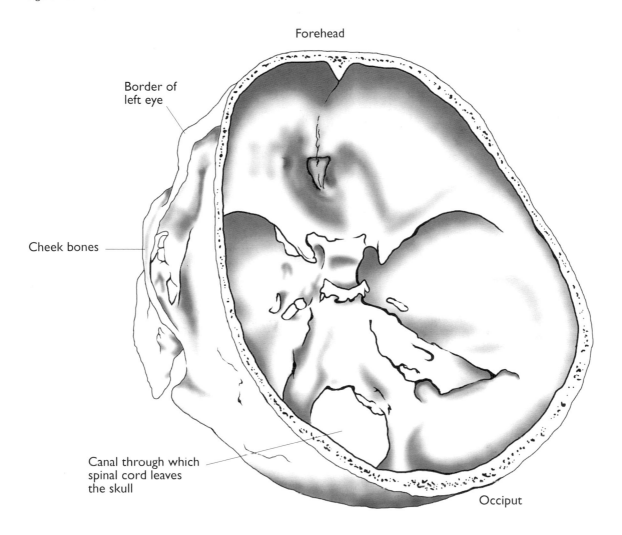

Forehead

Border of
left eye

Cheek bones

Canal through which
spinal cord leaves
the skull

Occiput

Ischaemia

Ischaemia refers to diminished supply of blood to an organ. The brain's supply of blood may be diminished by other injuries to parts of the body that supply blood to the head (eg to the chest) or by impaired perfusion.

Lobe

There are four lobes on each side of the brain. See entries for frontal, temporal, parietal and occipital lobe.

Localising

The term localising is used in two main ways:

- localising to pain
  When assessed on the Glasgow Coma Scale, the best response to the pain stimulus is to localise the pain, ie to brush away the source of the discomfort.

- localising value
  A deficit has localising value if it points to dysfunction in a particular area (eg a particular lobe, or part of a lobe) of the brain. There is an enormous scientific and medical literature tracing the connections between structural damage to areas of the brain and specific higher mental functions. It is important that the psychological assessments of patients, who are suspected of having a brain dysfunction, are obtained from a neuro-psychologist who has a grasp of this literature.

Magnetic Resonance Imaging (MRI)

This very advanced technique has been developed to achieve pictures of the inside of the brain. It does not involve any radiation (unlike x-rays) or injections (unlike blood flow imaging) and, therefore, is completely safe and non-invasive. The resolution of the images is excellent.

Maxillo-facial Injury

This term refers to damage to the soft tissues and bones of the face. Very commonly, these injuries occur at the same time as severe head injury. They may cause scarring with obvious cosmetic implications.

Memory

Memory is the process of storing, retaining and subsequently retrieving information. Memory is almost always damaged after a head injury.

Short term (or immediate) memory (STM) refers to the ability to hold information for the period during which it is actively being rehearsed (eg a telephone number). A common measure of STM is the ability to repeat back a list of numbers immediately after they have been heard (digit span). The average digit span in a normally functioning person is around 7. STM is surprisingly resistant to brain damage - patients may be severely amnesic yet have a normal STM.

Long term memory (LTM) is the term used for the process of retaining and recalling new information over a period of minutes, hours or longer. Many procedures have been devised to measure LTM, including the ability to learn lists of words or stories, or to recall complex pictures. In right-handed people, damage to the left side of the brain damages memory for verbal information, yet leaves memory for visuo-spatial information intact. Right-sided brain damage leads to the opposite pattern (impaired visuo-spatial, but preserved verbal memory).

Memory for things that happened many years ago is usually called remote memory.

Remembering to do things in the future is called prospective memory.

Motivation

Motivation refers to a condition of inner drive or energy which enables an individual to achieve goals or satisfy needs. This energy or drive can be disturbed by brain damage, particularly damage to the frontal parts of the brain. Patients are so easily dismissed as difficult, as clinicians may confuse a patient's experience of can't with won't (ie a confusion of inability or incapacity with lack of volition).

Motor Disorders

Motor disorders are disturbances of the ability to move or control muscle activity. They are common after very severe injury, but many patients go on to make remarkably good recovery of their motor capability. Deficits may involve any or all of the limbs or extremities, or trunk. They may include weakness (-paresis), inability to move (-plegia), or unco-ordinated or involuntary movements (for example chorea and athetosis).

MRI Scan

See magnetic resonance imaging.

Neuropsychologist

A neuropsychologist is a person with a degree in psychology and specialist training or experience in the practice of neuropsychology. The study and practice of neuropsychology involves the identification, analysis and treatment of the cognitive, behavioural and affective consequences of brain damage.

Neuropsychiatry

A neuropsychiatrist is a medically qualified person who has a higher qualification in psychiatry and who has special experience and training in the assessment and management of people who have psychiatric disorders consequent upon brain disease.

Occipital Lobes

The occipital lobes are the paired structures at the back of the outside surface of the brain which are vital to vision. Destruction of both structures leads to complete blindness (central blindness), but this is very rare after head injury. However, lesser degrees of visual impairment that result from damage to the occipital lobes are often seen.

Parietal Lobe

The parietal lobe is the part of the outer surface of the brain that is located above and behind the temples. The parietal lobe deals with the perception of touch and the integration of all the senses. Damage here can lead to varied consequences ranging from a difficulty in mathematics (dyscalculia) to a failure to recognise previously well-known faces.

Penetrating Head Injury

Most common in wartime, penetrating head injury is caused by a bullet or other missile. The effects differ from closed head injury. In the instance of penetrating head injury, the particular part of the brain destroyed determines the effects and these may be highly variable.

Perfusion

Perfusion is the process by which the brain is supplied with blood and, therefore, oxygen. The process is complicated and not yet fully understood. When blood pressure falls, or when raised pressure inside the skull creates resistance to normal blood flow, perfusion may be impaired. A brain which has been injured or damaged is less good at making normal adjustments in arterial size to allow the usual autoregulation of cerebral blood flow and this adds a further complication. Problems with cerebral blood flow, and perfusion and intra-cranial pressure, require skilled neurosurgical management.

Persistent Vegetative State (PVS)

PVS is the name given to a state that may follow very severe injury in which patients remain speechless and devoid of any meaningful contact with others. Patients show sleep-wake cycles but no evidence of conscious awareness. The condition is due to very extensive damage to the fibres under the cerebral cortex. Within the first 3-6 months after injury, some patients will proceed to a state of severe disability (see Glasgow Outcome Scale). Thereafter, and if well cared for, patients with these problems may survive indefinitely.

Personality

Personality is defined as a habitual tendency to feel, think, and behave in certain ways. Personality change is common after severe head injury, particularly when there is damage to the frontal or temporal lobes. The change is very often negative, ie unpleasant aspects of personality (eg aggression, boastfulness) that were suppressed or inhibited before the injury, may become prominent and may prevent the patient from returning to his or her previous occupation, or even to live with his or her family.

Post-concussion Syndrome

The post-concussion syndrome is a group of symptoms including: headache; dizziness; poor memory; impoverished concentration; anxiety; and depression. Some or all may be present after head injury. It is thought that these are a direct result of injury to the brain. If these symptoms and behaviours are unduly prolonged, it is thought that psychological factors are responsible. Neuropsychological testing can clarify the nature of the condition.

Post-traumatic Amnesia (PTA)

PTA is the period between the injury and the person regaining day-to-day memory so that the patient knows where he or she is and what happened to him or her. Any time spent in coma is included in determining the duration of PTA. The length of PTA is a good index of the severity of an underlying brain damage. Its significance is discussed in Annex D.

Post-traumatic Epilepsy

Epilepsy is a well recognised complication of head injury. Predictive factors for the development of epilepsy include: developing an intracranial haematoma; long post-traumatic amnesia; penetrating injury; existence of a depressed fracture; and the occurrence of a seizure within the first week after injury. Most patients who go on to develop epilepsy do so within the first five years after injury, but the risk is still present thereafter. Epilepsy has important psychosocial consequences for the sufferer (eg stigma, often an inability to have a licence to drive, the reluctance of employers to provide jobs) and some kinds of anticonvulsant medication cause significant side effects (eg slowing, poor memory).

Post-traumatic Neurosis

This syndrome consists of a characteristic group of symptoms of somatic (headache, vertigo), cognitive (memory, attention) and affective (anxiety, depression) natures. The syndrome may occur after minor head injury or after an accident in which there is no evidence of brain damage. Many patients who have symptoms of prolonged post-traumatic neurosis have indications in their experiences or history of a premorbid personality or of situational factors that would, in other circumstances, predispose them to develop a neurotic condition.

Post-traumatic Psychosis

Literally, this is a psychosis that follows head injury. It is a rare condition found more often after missile wounds than the blunt head injuries of civilian life. It has particular associations with damage to the temporal lobes of the brain and with dementia.

Prefrontal

The prefrontal area is at the extreme front of the brain. This part of the brain plays a part in many of the highest levels of human functioning and thinking such as planning, envisaging the consequences of actions, recognising the effects of one's behaviour on others. For instance, damage here can leave a patient looking perfectly normal, yet profoundly inert, concrete of thought and simplistic in ideation and behaviour. The resulting personal and social handicap can be very profound.

Psychosis

Psychosis is the term for a severe disorder of behaviour, feeling and thinking. Contact with reality is impaired, and there may be hallucinations and delusions. The psychoses may be classified into organic (dementia) and functional (depression and schizophrenia), and the basis of causology and the pattern of symptoms, signs and behaviours. Both are very rare sequelae of blunt head injury.

Psychosocial Problems

The changes in behaviour and affective status in a patient, following head injury, and the effect these changes have on those around the patient, particularly his or her immediate family, are described as psychosocial problems. They may be profound and productive of long-term disability and cumulative handicap.

Rehabilitation

Rehabilitation is the process after immediate medical and/or surgical care by which a patient is assisted in achieving his or her full physical, cognitive, behavioural, social and occupational potential. The two main phases are acute (starting just after initial medical and or surgical care) and transitional (bridging the gap back to community re-entry).

Retrograde Amnesia (RA)

Retrograde amnesia describes a period of amnesia for events before an injury. This is almost always much less than the period of post-traumatic amnesia and is not as good a predictor of outcome as PTA. However, given that there is a period of RA and PTA after significant head injury, its significance is that a patient who suffers a retrograde amnesia will not remember the moment of impact nor usually the events leading up to the injury.

Secondary Brain Damage

A range of complications that may follow the damage resulting from a primary impact or injury. Common complications include: brain swelling; bleeding inside the head or brain; infection of the brain tissues or their coverings.

Severity (of blunt head injury)

The main indices of the severity of a head injury are the duration of coma (assessed using the Glasgow Coma Scale and the duration of post-traumatic amnesia). When there is a need for an intracranial operation, that in itself suggests that the injury was serious.

Skull Fracture

Skull fracture is a common complication of head injury. A linear fracture may be of little significance of itself. The problem is that such a fracture may act as a route by which infection can enter the brain or its coverings, or it may cause transection of an artery directly beneath the skull, thereby causing acute haemorrhage and the formation of a haematoma inside the skull which presses on the brain tissue causing secondary damage. A depressed fracture is serious, as a route for infection and a source of direct brain damage by in-driven fragments of the skull.

Spect (Single Photon Emission Computed Tomography)

Spect is a way of imaging the distribution of blood flow in the brain. The images give pictures of slices of the brain (hence tomography). It is a form of functional imaging unlike CT and MRI scanning that are structural imaging.

Speech Disturbance

A distinction should be made between problems of speech (dysarthria or anarthria) and of language (dysphasia or aphasia). Both happen commonly, but through different kinds of brain damage. Speech problems are probably more common than the language problems, but both can interfere with a person's return to work after brain injury. Speech therapists are skilled at dealing with both types of problem.

Speech Therapy

Speech therapy is a range of treatments administered by speech therapists. These therapists are specialists in helping patients to deal with a wide range of disorders of communication including dysphasia.

Temporal Lobes

The temporal lobes are the parts of the outer and middle aspects of the brain that are located adjacent to the temples. Damage to the temporal lobes can lead to cognitive, behaviour, and physical disorders. The cognitive disorder is that of the memory; the behaviour disorders range widely, including changes in anger and sexuality; and frequently, the physical disorder is epilepsy. The memory disorder is likely to be lateralised; a left temporal disorder leading to disturbed verbal memory but preserved non-verbal memory. The opposite pattern is found with right temporal damage (assuming, in both cases, that the victim is right-handed).

Ventricles (cerebral ventricles)

The ventricles are fluid-filled spaces inside the brain. They contain cerebro-spinal fluid and can be seen on brain images. Enlargement of the ventricles can indicate increased pressure inside the brain or the loss of brain cells.

White Matter

The white matter is the nerve fibres of the brain. These carry the information around the brain. On naked eye inspection, they are glistening white. They may be contrasted with the grey matter which is composed of collections of nerve cell bodies rather than the fibres of these cells that form the white matter.

Severity and
Outcome Scales

THE GLASGOW OUTCOME SCALE

14   This scale has been widely used in research and is very useful in that context for giving a broad impression of outcome very quickly. However, it is much too crude for ordinary clinical and for medico-legal evaluation. For example, it has been shown that patients classified as making a Good Recovery (GR) may have very considerable deficits. Equally, it has been shown that many patients who achieve the GR category will not be able to resume employment.

15   The scale classifies all individuals in one of five categories and these are:

- **Death**
- **Vegetative State**
  In this category, patients show no evidence from their behaviour of cerebral cortical function. Patients may open their eyes, and sometimes follow with their eyes, and may make postural adjustments. However, they never speak nor make any response that is psychologically meaningful. Therefore, they do not obey simple commands, and do not utter simple words.

- **Severe Disability** (conscious but dependent)
  At this level of severity, patients are dependent on another person for some activity during every 24 hours. The worst affected are physically disabled, or may show marked dysphasia as the major handicap. The presence of marked handicaps is associated with severely restricted mental activity. Nonetheless, some patients may be physically well but so affected mentally that they require permanent supervision.

- **Moderate Disability** (independent but disabled)
  At this level, sufferers are able to look after themselves. They can travel by public transport, and some may be capable of sheltered work. Most people who are moderately disabled as a result of a head injury have:

  - memory deficits;

  - personality changes;

  - hemiparesis;

  - ataxia;

  - dysphasia; and/or

  - epilepsy.

- **Good Recovery**
  The definition of this category in the scale indicates that this need not imply the restoration of all normal functions. However, patients are able to participate in normal social life and could return to work (but may not have done so). Nonetheless, in practice, Good Recovery is often used to denote a better state than Moderate Disability and research has found that patients in this category may have considerable residual problems including inability to resume work on the open market.

THE GLASGOW COMA SCALE

Introduction

16   The Glasgow Coma Scale is used to measure the level of responsiveness of patients after injury or other event. Thus, it provides a measure of the severity of brain injury (although post-traumatic amnesia must also be considered). It is used as a tool for monitoring patients and enables changes in their levels of responsiveness to be recognised and compared quickly and in a way that is reliable despite being carried out by different testers (provided they are proficient in the techniques used to apply the tests and classifying the results). This comparative capacity is important as deterioration raises the question of whether there is a developing intracranial condition that could require emergency intervention.

The Scale

17   Responsiveness is measured in three domains:

Eye Opening (E)

Spontaneous	4
To speech	3
To pain*	2
Nil	1

Best Motor Response (M)

Obeys	6
Localizes pain*	5
Withdraws from pain*	4
Abnormal flexion*	3
Extensor response*	2
Nil*	1

Verbal Response (V)

Orientated	5
Confused conversation	4
Inappropriate words	3
Incomprehensible sounds	2
Nil	1

*A standard but harmless pain stimulus is administered, usually by rolling an object over the eyebrow.

Scoring

18   The total score is E + M + V giving a worst possible total of 3 and a best of 15. Sometimes points 3 and 4 on the M scale are collapsed reducing the total range to 3-14.

The Significance of the Score

19   It has become common to ascribe the following severity levels to GCS scores:

Head Injury Severity	GCS
• Very Severe	3-5
• Severe	6-8
• Moderate	9-12
• Minor	13-15

20 Coma is defined by a GCS of less than 8 (or 8 in some circumstances). Research has shown that the prognosis after head injury is directly related to the GCS and it is particularly poor in patients who:

- have or develop a GCS of 8 or less;

- show a deterioration of GCS of 2 or more points, particularly if this takes the GCS below 8;

- develop a fixed dilated (blown) pupil;

- develop lateralising neurological signs.

21 Whether or not this classification is accepted, the duration of post-traumatic amnesia should not be overlooked as a guide to severity.

THE DURATION OF POST-TRAUMATIC AMNESIA

22 Duration of post-traumatic amnesia (PTA) is a key yardstick of the severity of brain injury.

23 PTA is the period between the injury and when a patient regains day-to-day memory to the extent of knowing where he or she is, and what happened to him or her. It includes any period of coma.

24 In some cases, there may be an apparent conflict between the clinical findings. One such circumstance is that in which the patient has a long PTA (suggesting severe injury) while the Glasgow Coma Scale score was never particularly low (suggesting the injury was not severe). In these circumstances, the PTA is the preferred index. This is because research has shown that there is a group of patients which fits this picture but whose head injuries are severe despite the good GCS.

25 The significance of PTA duration may be gauged in the following way:

- **PTA 1 Day or Less**
  Expect quick and full recovery after appropriate management. A few patients may show persisting disability, usually resulting from the post-concussion syndrome.

- **PTA Over 1 Day, Less Than 1 Week**
  The recovery period may be more prolonged - weeks or months. Most patients will recover fully given good management.

- **PTA 1 To 2 Weeks**
  Recovery takes many months. Many patients will be left with residual problems even after the recovery process has apparently ended. Patients can be reasonably optimistic about their recovery of functions (eg taking up employment, social activities, etc) if they have good management.

- **PTA 2 To 4 Weeks**
  The process of recovery is likely to be very prolonged - one year or even a little longer would not be unusual. Permanent deficits

are likely. There must be increasing pessimism about a patient's recovery of day-to-day functions when PTA reaches these lengths.

- **PTA Over 4 Weeks**
  Permanent deficits, indeed significant disability, are now almost certain. Management is less a matter of promoting recovery and more one of long-term retraining and management.

(C)CMS Ltd 1989. Revised 1991. (C)CMS Ltd 1995.

OTHER ASSESSMENT TOOLS

Introduction

26   Listed below are the names and sources of three assessment schedules that are useful in determining the severity and nature of the problems faced by individual patients.

General Assessment of Mental State

Mini Mental State

27   This rating in scale is used widely to assess cognitive functioning. It focuses on orientation, attention and memory. It is available in the Journal of Psychiatric Research (Folstein M F, Folstein S E, McHugh P R, (1975). Journal of Psychiatric Research 12: 189-198).

Early Onset Dementia

Cape Procedures

28   This scale is used to assess elderly people. Copies are obtainable from the Manual of the Clifton Assessment Procedures for the Elderly (Pattie A, Gilleard C, (1979), Hodder and Stoughton).

Huntington's Disease

The Functional Rating Scale for Huntington's Disease

29   This is a relatively straightforward scale for assessing the disabilities of people who have Huntington's Disease. It is available in Movement Disorders by Marsden C D, Fahn S, (editors) (1982), New York, Butterworth Scientific.

*The Expert Advisory Group
and the Service Visitors*

THE EXPERT ADVISORY GROUP

Dr Willie Barker

Willie Barker is a consultant neuropsychiatrist and is Head of the Neurobehavioural Service at Newcastle upon Tyne City Health NHS Trust. He has a special interest in Huntington's Disease and he deals with all aspects of the disease from genetic counselling, predictive testing and early diagnosis through to the management of people who have Huntington's Disease itself. He deals with the neuropsychiatric consequences of all types of acquired brain injury, and runs a regional neurobehavioural unit.

Dr Kenneth Barrett

Ken Barrett is a consultant neuropsychiatrist and clinical director for mental health within North Staffordshire Combined Healthcare NHS Trust. He heads a neuropsychiatry service which includes responsibility for adults with acquired brain injury, early onset dementia and Huntington's Disease, covering a population of approximately half a million. He is senior clinical lecturer and former senior lecturer in neuropsychiatry at the School of Post-graduate Medicine, Keele University, where he developed the diploma and masters programmes in postgraduate psychiatry.

Mr William Bingley

William Bingley is a lawyer by training and, since 1990, he has been the Chief Executive of the Mental Health Act Commission. He was Legal Director of MIND (National Association for Mental Health) from 1983 to 1989 when he was seconded to the Department of Health as executive secretary of the working group preparing the Mental Health Act Code of Practice which was published in 1990.

He was a member of the Secretary of State's working group on the future of high security psychiatric provision and is currently a co-opted member of the BMA Medical Ethics Committee and has observer status on the Law Society's Mental Health and Disability Sub-committee.

Dr Neil Brooks

Neil Brooks is a consultant neuropsychologist to Brain Injury Services and also manages a private practice involving clinical, medico-legal and research activities. He is currently President of Headway, the National Head Injuries Association, President of the European Brain Injury Society, and Chairman of the British Association of Brain Injury Case Managers. He was previously a professor in the Department of Psychological Medicine, University of Glasgow, and is a past president of the International Brain Injury Society.

Ms Jill Cox

Jill Cox is both a general and mental health nurse. Presently, she is general manager of Elderly Services at City and Hackney Community Services NHS Trust. Jill has a special interest in the provision of services for people with both physical and mental health needs. Previously, she worked for several years as a community psychiatric nurse, experiencing first hand the complexities of delivering appropriate care to clients and their carers.

Jill is currently undertaking research into the information which influences the decision-making of clients and their carers when they are faced with the prospect of continuing care.

Dr Stuart Cumella

Stuart Cumella is senior research fellow and director of the Centre for Research and Information in Mental Disability (CRIMD) at the University of Birmingham. His academic background is in economics, politics, and social administration. He is a qualified social worker, and has worked as a researcher in central government and with the Medical Research Council, and as a manager in the NHS. Stuart Cumella's current research interests concern the impact of the internal markets for health and social care on mental health services, the development of outcome measures for learning disability services, primary care and social work, and the mental health of homeless children.

Mr Giles Emerson

Giles Emerson is a professional writer whose clients include most of the major government departments, as well as corporations in the private sector. He writes occasionally for *The Times* and *The Independent*, usually but not exclusively on the subject of the use and abuse of English, advocating a simple and direct approach. He has recently been commissioned to write a book on how to survive as a professional writer. Giles was educated at Exeter School in Devon and at Exeter College, Oxford, where he read English Language and Literature, graduating in 1978. He subsequently worked as a sub-editor on magazines about DIY, Gardening, War, and Sex among other subjects for Marshall Cavendish Partworks in London. In 1980, he joined the Central Office of Information as a writer and editor, where he gained much of his experience of writing for government organisations. In September 1984, Giles left the COI to learn more about the private sector and worked as a writer in a leading public relations company in Fleet Street for a year. In September 1985, he left London to set up his own business in Shropshire, where he works today.

Mr Clive Evers

Clive Evers is Director of Information and Education at the Alzheimer's Disease Society which he joined as Information and Training Officer in 1988. He has published a public information service for carers and professionals which now responds to 23,000 enquiries annually on all aspects of Alzheimer's Disease and other dementias. Currently, he is chairman of the Creutzfeldt Jakob Disease Support Network.

Mr Michael Gardiner

Mike Gardiner is currently Area Manager (Winchester) for the Social Services Department of Hampshire County Council. However, with the remodelling of the department as a result of Local Government reorganisation, he is to become Area Director (Winchester and Andover).

Mike qualified as a social worker in 1973 and since then has undertaken a course in groupwork theory and practice at the University of Bristol in 1980 and obtained a Master of Social Science Degree in 'social services management' at the University of Birmingham in 1990.

In his current role, Mike is responsible for the management of all social services within his administrative area, including residential and day services, fieldwork, hospital and health service based services for all client groups. He was also one of a small team of Hampshire managers responsible for implementation of the NHS and Community Care Act 1990.

Mrs Zena Muth

Zena Muth is the present Deputy Director of the NHS Health Advisory Service (HAS). She is a Department of Health civil servant and is responsible for the day to day management of the HAS. Since taking up appointment in 1993, she has held particular responsibility for the management and organisation of the NHS Drug Advisory Service, which is a component of the HAS. Zena has also undertaken a number of HAS visits and managed the team that conducted a review of Ashworth Special Hospital.

Mr Ted Riley

Ted Riley is a contracts manager for Avon Health Authority. He is an occupational therapist and previously has worked in all areas of mental health services. More recently, he has moved into general management and held managerial posts in mental health and acute services.

In his post at Avon Health Authority, he commissions and purchases services for adults with mental illness, and child and adolescent mental health services. He has also worked extensively for the NHS Health Advisory Service on several thematic reviews.

Dr Richard Williams

Richard Williams is the present Director of the NHS Health Advisory Service (HAS). Upon appointment in 1992, he was required to reposition the HAS so that it worked in accordance with the reformed health service. One of the new activities of the HAS, which he has developed, are the Thematic Reviews. Four of these have been completed and another seven are either close to completion or in progress. Richard Williams is also a Consultant Child and Adolescent Psychiatrist at the Bristol Royal Hospital for Sick Children, where he developed an extensive liaison and consultation service with other community childcare workers and the child health services. His particular clinical interests include the psychological impacts and treatment of life-threatening and chronic physical disorders and he has extensive experience of working with families which have experienced psychological trauma. He has been involved in service management over a number of years and has a particular interest and experience in the theory and practice of leadership and the selection and development of leaders. Along with the Director of the Institute of Health Services Management, he inspired the creation of a Leadership Development Programme for Top Managers in Mental Health in 1994. Consequent on his work with the HAS, he has developed particular experience in the challenges posed to health authorities in purchasing comprehensive health services for mentally ill and elderly people.

THE SERVICE VISITORS

The visits to the six selected services were undertaken by members of the expert advisory group together with Deborah Evans and Jim Leivers.

Ms Deborah Evans

Deborah Evans is Director of Contract Management for Avon Health Authority. She has worked as a commissioner of healthcare since November 1989 and is actively involved in developing a mental health strategy for Avon.

Deborah has been associated with the NHS Health Advisory Service for the past three years, and has participated as a member of visiting teams for general and thematic reviews. She also leads a session on HAS training courses for secondees.

Mr Jim Leivers

Currently, Jim Leivers works as an Assistant Director of Social Services for the East Riding of Yorkshire Council. He has operational responsibility for all areas of social work activity. Prior to this, he was employed as an Assistant Director by the then Humberside County Council in which he had responsibility for delivering services to children and families. Jim Leivers has a particular interest in developing effective working partnerships between health and social services.

Printed in the United Kingdom for the Stationery Office
Dd 0301389   2/97   3400   65536   365490   03/37261